SRA Open Court Reading

Reading and Writing Workbook

Program Authors

Carl Bereiter
Ann Brown
Joe Campione
Iva Carruthers
Robbie Case
Jan Hirshberg
Marilyn Jager Adams
Anne McKeough
Michael Pressley
Marsha Roit
Marlene Scardamalia
Gerald H. Treadway, Jr.

A Division of The McGraw-Hill Companies

Columbus, Ohio

SRA/McGraw-Hill

A Division of The McGraw·Hill Companies

Copyright © 2000 by SRA/McGraw-Hill.

Send all inquiries to:
SRA/McGraw-Hill
8787 Orion Place
Columbus, Ohio 43240

Printed in the United States of America.

ISBN 0-02-831068-3

15 16 17 18 19 20 DBH 10 09 08 07 06

Table of Contents

Unit 4

Unit 5

Unit 6

Author's Purpose

Focus Writers always have a reason for writing a story.

The author's reason for writing a story is called the **author's purpose**.

- The author's purpose can be to inform, explain, entertain, or persuade. An author can have more than one purpose for writing.

- The author's purpose affects the details, descriptions, pictures, and dialogue that are included in a story.

Identify Look through "Class President." What do you think the author's main purpose was for writing this selection?

_____

What makes you think this was the purpose?

_____

_____

_____

_____

How successful do you think the author was in this purpose?

_____

_____

_____

_____

Practice Read the following paragraphs and write the author's purpose for each.

1. The story "Alice in Wonderland" was originally written by Lewis Carroll as a gift for a young child named Alice. The story included his own illustrations. These were very different from any of the illustrations that were done later when he expanded the story into a book-length version.

   Author's purpose: _____

2. I invented a new game. You need four bases, in-line skates for all players, a soccer ball, and a bat. First, set up the bases like in baseball—first, second, third, and home. Then, have a pitcher throw the soccer ball to the batter. The batter tries to hit the ball with the bat. As in baseball, the batter has three strikes before he or she is out. If the batter is successful, he or she skates around the bases. Doesn't it sound like fun?

   Author's purpose: _____

Apply Take some factual information that you know or have heard in the news and use it to write an opening paragraph for an entertaining story.

_____

_____

_____

_____

_____

_____

_____

_____

Name _____   Date _____

Drawing Conclusions

Focus Good readers know how to draw conclusions about characters or events they read about in a story.

> **Drawing conclusions** means putting information together to make a statement about a character or event in a story. Readers can draw conclusions based on
> - how a character behaves or what he or she says.
> - when and where a story takes place.
>
> While a conclusion may not be directly stated in the text, it should be supported by examples in the story.

Identify Look through "Class President." What conclusions can you draw about a character or event in the story? Find information in the story that helped you draw your conclusions.

Page: _____

Conclusion about a character: _____

_____

Information that supports the conclusion: _____

_____

Page: _____

Conclusion about an event: _____

_____

Information that supports the conclusion: _____

_____

Practice and Apply Think of the names of three things, such
as a computer, a horse, and a soccer ball. Then, write three
statements about each thing, without using the things' names.
(Use the word "it" instead.)

1. _____

   _____

   _____

2. _____

   _____

   _____

3. _____

   _____

   _____

Show your statements to a classmate. See whether your
classmate can draw the right conclusions and identify the
things you wrote about.

Analyzing Character Traits

Focus Writers provide clues to a character's personality by showing how he or she talks and acts, and by what others say about the character.

> **Character traits** can be discovered by paying attention to the character's actions and words and by noticing what others say and think about the character.

Identify Look through "Class President" for examples of ways that the author reveals information about his characters.

Page: _____   Character: _____

Example: _____

_____

_____

_____

_____

_____

Page: _____   Character: _____

Example: _____

_____

_____

_____

_____

_____

Practice Write a conversation in which you and your best friend are having an argument. Explain what the argument is about. Include details about how you both feel and how the two of you react to the situation.

_____

_____

_____

_____

_____

_____

_____

_____

_____

Apply Answer the following questions about the passage you wrote above.

What does the passage tell the reader about you?

_____

_____

_____

What does the passage tell the reader about your friend?

_____

_____

_____

_____

Root Words with the Suffix -tion

Focus Writers can build their vocabularies by learning how to add affixes to root words to make new words and change word meanings.

- An **affix** is a word part added to the beginning or end of a root word to change its meaning.
- A **root word** is a stand-alone word to which an affix can be added.
- A **suffix** is an affix added to the end of a root word.
- The **suffix -tion** means "act or state of being."
- If the root word ends with an *e*, you must change the final *e* to *a* before adding *-tion*, or drop the final *e* before adding *-ion*.

Root Word	Suffix	Meaning	New Word	Meaning
determine	-tion	act or state of being	*determination*	act of being determined

Practice Write new words by adding the suffix *-tion*, or *-ion*, to the root words below.

Root Words	New Words
1. dedicate	_____
2. imitate	_____
3. imagine	_____
4. react	_____
5. predict	_____
6. elect	_____
7. suggest	_____

Identify the root word and write the meaning for each word
listed below.

Word	Root Word	Word Meaning
8. creation	_____	_____
9. conservation	_____	_____
10. nomination	_____	_____
11. exploration	_____	_____
12. infection	_____	_____

Apply Write a sentence for each of the new words above.

1. _____

_____

2. _____

_____

3. _____

_____

4. _____

_____

5. _____

_____

Name _____ Date _____

Prepositions and Prepositional Phrases

Focus Writers use prepositional phrases to add details
to their writing and to make their thoughts clearer.

- A **preposition** shows how one word is related to another
  word in the sentence.

- Some common prepositions are *at, in, on, to, for, from,
  with, until, before,* and *after.*

- A **prepositional phrase** always begins with a preposition
  and is followed by a noun or a pronoun and any of its
  modifiers.

- Prepositional phrases are used as adjectives and adverbs
  in a sentence. A prepositional phrase that describes a noun
  should appear as close to the noun as possible.

Identify Look through "Class President" for examples
of prepositional phrases. Write the page number and the
complete sentence. Underline each prepositional phrase.

Page: _____

Sentence: _____

_____

Page: _____

Sentence: _____

_____

Page: _____

Sentence: _____

_____

Practice Read the sentences below. Then rewrite each sentence so that the prepositional phrase that describes a noun appears as close as possible to that noun.

1. A woman crossed the street in a raincoat.

   _____

2. The sweater was lost with blue and white ribbons.

   _____

3. The flowers need some water in the blue vase.

   _____

4. A green car roared down the hill with a white top.

   _____

Apply Choose three of the prepositions shown in the box below. Use each in a sentence as the beginning of a prepositional phrase.

near	at	for
in	after	with

1. _____

   _____

2. _____

   _____

3. _____

   _____

Making Inferences

The Marble Champp

Focus When writers don't include all the information about a character or a story event, readers must make inferences in order to get the whole picture.

> Readers can use information from a story, along with their own experience or knowledge, to **make inferences** that help them understand a character or event more completely.

Identify Find two sentences in "The Marble Champ" that give you some information about Lupe. Write the page numbers and sentences. Then, write a word or phrase that would describe Lupe's character, based on the sentences you wrote.

Page: _____

Sentence: _____

_____

What the reader can infer about Lupe from this sentence: _____

_____

_____

Page: _____

Sentence: _____

_____

What the reader can infer about Lupe from this sentence: _____

_____

_____

_____

Practice Read the paragraph below. Then, write down what you can infer about the person in the paragraph.

> None of the other students noticed Marty. Most of the time he kept his eyes down and looked at his desk. If, by accident, someone did catch his eye, he always blushed furiously and looked away immediately. When the teacher asked a question, Marty would sometimes raise his hand. But when the teacher called on him, no one could understand what he was saying because he spoke so softly.

Inference made about Marty: _____

_____

Apply Choose a word from the box below. Write a paragraph giving information about a character you invent. When making inferences about the character, the reader of your paragraph should be able to infer the word you chose. Do not use the word in your paragraph.

clownish	loud	friendly

_____

_____

_____

_____

_____

_____

Name _____ Date _____

Recognize and Analyze Story Setting

Focus It is important for writers to provide vivid settings for their stories so that readers can picture where and when the events are taking place.

> **Setting** is the time and place in which the events of a story occur. An author makes the setting more interesting by describing how a place *looks*, *sounds*, *smells*, and *feels*. In addition to the general setting of the story, there may be more specific settings where action takes place, such as the character's home or school.

Identify Look through "The Marble Champ." Select a specific setting from the story and list some of the details that the author uses to describe it.

Setting	Details That Describe Setting

Practice Think about two or three of your favorite stories. What is the setting for each story? Complete the chart below.

THE SETTINGS FOR MY FAVORITE STORIES

Story	Where and When It Takes Place	Details That Describe Setting

Apply Write the first paragraph of a story that takes place in a setting that is familiar to you, such as your house, your room, or your classroom. Include details in your writing that will help readers visualize when and where the story is taking place.

_____

_____

_____

_____

_____

_____

_____

Consonant Before *-le* Syllable Pattern

Focus Words that end with the same sound can be spelled in different ways.

> There are many rules to help us learn how to spell words, but when the words end in *-le, -el, -al, -il,* or *-ol* there is no rule. These words must be studied individually and their spellings memorized.

Practice Look at the following words. Think about and list three things they have in common.

settle	middle	bundle	fumble	pebble	trifle

1. _____

_____

2. _____

_____

3. _____

_____

Write three more words that can be added to this list.

4. _____

5. _____

6. _____

Read the following clues. Write a word that fits the clue and ends with a consonant -*le* syllable.

7. _____ This is something that appears after it rains, and you can jump in it.

8. _____ This is what you do when you tell on someone.

9. _____ This type of puzzling question always has a clever answer.

10. _____ This is the name of a book or a movie.

11. _____ A fire makes this noise as it is burning.

12. _____ You make this sound when you purse your lips and blow.

13. _____ This is a synonym for the word *laugh*.

14. _____ This is just above your foot.

15. _____ This is a small stone.

Apply Choose two words that end in the consonant before -*le* syllable pattern and write a sentence for each word.

_____

_____

_____

_____

_____

_____

_____

Name _____   Date _____

Nouns

Focus A **noun** is a word that names a person, a place, a thing, or an idea.

> Here are some examples of nouns from the story:
> - **People:** Alfonso, opponent, President of the Fresno Marble Association
> - **Places:** backyard, middle of the outfield, Fresno
> - **Things:** sports, thumb, pizza
> - **Ideas:** truth, instinct

Identify Read the fourth paragraph on page 41 of "The Marble Champ." On the lines below, list the nouns from this paragraph.

List the nouns that name people: _____

_____

List the nouns that name places: _____

_____

List the nouns that name things: _____

_____

Nouns *(continued)*

Practice Use the information in the story to fill in the blanks in the following sentences with appropriate nouns.

1. Lupe practiced every _____ until she was

   ready for the _____.

2. Her _____ was impressed with how hard

   _____ could hit the _____.

3. _____ felt embarrassed when all the

   _____ in the _____

   came up to congratulate her.

4. They set the _____ on the _____

   in the _____ for all to see.

Apply Fill in the chart with nouns you can see in your classroom. Write them in the appropriate columns.

People	Places	Things

Author's Point of View

Focus Writers must decide from whose **point of view** they will tell a story.

- Stories told through the eyes of a character in the story are in the **first-person** point of view. A first-person narrator uses words such as *I, me, we, us, our,* and *my.*

- Stories told through the eyes of an outside storyteller are in the **third-person** point of view. A third-person narrator uses words such as *he, she, him, her, them, theirs, his,* and *hers.*

Practice and Apply Read each paragraph and write whether it is in the first-person or third-person point of view. Then, rewrite the paragraph, changing the point of view.

1. The room was quiet and empty. As Steven entered, he could not help but feel frightened. However, he was quite curious.

   Point of view: _____

   New paragraph: _____

   _____

   _____

   _____

   _____

   _____

   _____

   _____

   _____

2. Last week a new girl moved to our block. At first, we didn't like her too much. Then she let us ride her new mountain bike. We changed our minds about her.

Point of view: _____

New paragraph: _____

_____

_____

_____

_____

_____

_____

3. "Never in my wildest dreams did I expect to see you here!" shouted Andy in surprise. I just stood up and smiled. It was good to see Andy after so many months.

Point of view: _____

New paragraph: _____

_____

_____

_____

_____

_____

_____

Name _____ Date _____

Identifying Purpose of Text

Focus Good readers can identify the **author's purpose**, or reason, for writing a story. Remember, an author can have more than one purpose for writing a story.

An author may write:

- **to inform,** or to give an explanation, information, or directions. Textbooks, encyclopedias, and other nonfiction books, such as how-to books, contain informational text.

- **to entertain,** or to make a reader laugh, feel scared, or otherwise enjoy reading about the characters and situations. Authors write stories, novels, and plays to entertain.

- **to influence,** or to persuade the reader to do something or think in a certain way. Advertisements and editorials, as well as some nonfiction books, are written to influence or persuade.

Identify If you didn't know anything about the story "Juggling" except its title, what might you think the author's purpose was for writing it? Why?

_____

_____

_____

_____

_____

_____

_____

Practice Read each passage below. Write the author's
purpose and give the reason for your decision.

1. The attic door creaked as Susie opened it. The light was dim,
   but she could see that cobwebs covered the old furniture
   and boxes. She approached a large trunk, hoping to find her
   old doll quickly. All of a sudden—Bang!—the door to the
   attic slammed shut!

   _____

2. Chop one head of cabbage, two carrots, and a large onion.
   Place the vegetables in a large pot, cover them with water,
   and boil them for ten minutes. Reduce the heat and add one
   can of stewed tomatoes, some salt, pepper, and spices.
   Simmer for 45 minutes.

   _____

Apply Write a review of "Juggling." Your purpose is to
persuade others to read it or not to read it.

_____

_____

_____

_____

_____

_____

_____

_____

_____

_____

_____

Pronouns

Focus Writers use **pronouns** in place of nouns to make their sentences clearer and to avoid repeating nouns.

A pronoun that is the subject of a sentence is a **subject pronoun**. This pronoun is in the **nominative case**. The subject pronouns are *I, you, he, she, it, we,* and *they.*

A pronoun that follows an action verb in a sentence is an **object pronoun**. This pronoun is in the **objective case.** The object pronouns are *me, you, him, her, it, us,* and *them.*

Object pronouns can be

- **direct objects,** meaning they directly follow an action verb.
  Bill called *me.*

- **objects of prepositions,** meaning they are the pronoun in a prepositional phrase.
  Bill wrote a note to *me.*

Practice Circle the subject pronouns and underline the object pronouns in these sentences.

1. Salvador asked me to come over on Sunday.

2. The salesclerk handed the large package to him.

3. He reminded us to pack a lunch for Tuesday's field trip.

4. Scott spotted the squirrels in the yard and chased after them.

5. I was going to bring a flashlight, but I forgot it.

6. Thomas followed him into the classroom to return the book.

7. It was wonderful to have you spend the weekend.

8. We gave her a new watch for good luck.

Pronouns (*continued*)

Apply Rewrite each sentence below, replacing the underlined words with subject or object pronouns.

1. <u>Bob and Lisa</u> called Marianne and invited <u>Marianne</u> to the party.

_____

_____

_____

2. Belinda expected <u>Mrs. Zimmerman</u> to arrive at any moment.

_____

_____

_____

3. The principal presented the spirit award to <u>the cheerleaders</u>.

_____

_____

_____

4. Grandmother wanted <u>Adrienne and me</u> to come over.

_____

_____

_____

5. Coach Riggs gave the towels to <u>Jodie and me</u>.

_____

_____

_____

Name _____ Date _____

Sequence

Focus To help readers make sense of what they read, writers show the **sequence**, or order, of events by using time and order words.

Time and order words provide readers with clues about which events happen before or after others in a story.

- Some words that indicate time are *yesterday, tomorrow, morning, night, moment, minute, suddenly,* and *last year.*

- Some words that indicate order are *first, last, after, next, finally,* and *then.*

Identify Look through "The Abacus Contest." Find examples of words or phrases used by the author to indicate a certain amount of time, a certain time of day, or the order in which events take place.

1. Page: _____   Paragraph: _____

Word or phrase: _____

_____

2. Page: _____   Paragraph: _____

Word or phrase: _____

_____

3. Page: _____   Paragraph: _____

Word or phrase: _____

_____

Practice Read each sentence. Then, fill in the blanks with
a word or phrase that indicates time or order.

1. We are going to the movies, and _____
   we are going out to dinner.

2. I will call my friend _____ I do my homework.

3. We waited in line impatiently, but _____
   they let us in.

4. _____ I went to school, but this week
   is a vacation.

5. My birthday was _____.

Apply Write a paragraph about the things you did yesterday.
Be sure to include time and order words to help the reader
understand when each event took place.

_____

_____

_____

_____

_____

_____

_____

_____

_____

_____

_____

Inflections

Focus To correctly spell the endings that are added
to root words, you must sometimes change the spellings
of the root words.

Two common endings that are added to root words are *-ed*
and *-ing*. Adding the *-ed* ending to a word shows something
that happened in the past. Adding the *-ing* ending to a word
shows something that's happening right now.

- When adding the ending *-ed* or *-ing* to a word that ends
  in a silent *e*, drop the final *e*.

- When adding the ending *-ed* to a word that ends in a *y*,
  change the *y* to an *i*.

- When adding the ending *-ed* or *-ing* to a word that
  ends in a consonant, you sometimes have to double
  the final consonant.

Identify Read through the first page of "The Abacus
Contest." List the first eight words you read that end in *-ed*.
Then, write the root word for each.

1. _____   _____

2. _____   _____

3. _____   _____

4. _____   _____

5. _____   _____

6. _____   _____

7. _____   _____

8. _____   _____

Inflections *(continued)*

Practice Look at the words you just listed. Answer the following questions about the words.

1. For which root words would you drop the final *e* before adding the *-ing* ending? Write the words with the *-ing* ending.

   _____

2. For which root word would you double the final consonant before adding the *-ing* ending? Write that word with the *-ing* ending.

   _____

3. What change, if any, would you make to the remaining root words before adding the *-ing* ending? Write those words with the *-ing* ending.

   _____

   _____

Apply Write an account of a dream or daydream that you had recently. You may write it in the past or present tense, but be sure to use the correct spellings of the *-ed* and *-ing* endings.

   _____

   _____

   _____

   _____

   _____

   _____

   _____

   _____

   _____

Complete Sentences

The Abacus Contest

Focus Writers use complete sentences so readers can easily understand what the writers want to say.

- A **complete sentence** has a subject and a predicate. A **subject** tells *who* or *what* the sentence is about. A **predicate** tells *what happens* or *has happened.*
  Our grandfather visits us every summer.

- An incomplete sentence is one that is missing a subject or a predicate.
  Our grandfather. Visits us every summer.

Identify Read the paragraphs below. Underline the incomplete sentences.

　　Toshi and I walk to school together every morning. Go through the park and across the river. Then we turn left and walk past the post office. Mrs. Rivera, who is in charge of running the post office, always waves to us. At the door to the school, the principal Mr. Hawkins. Out of breath, we run through the door. Just in time for our first class, which is Spanish.

　　My cat Toby is a real character. Always making me laugh. He loves to play. Chasing his toy mouse around the floor. Toby wakes me up every morning. He jumps on my bed and meows softly. Some mornings. I don't want to get up. Toby meows louder and louder. After breakfast. Toby and I are ready for another great day.

Practice Underline the subject in each sentence below.

1. The science fair starts at three o'clock this afternoon.

2. I worked on my science project until ten o'clock this morning.

3. Mrs. Jefferson says that I have a good chance of winning a ribbon for my project.

4. Six teachers will judge the science fair.

Put two lines under the predicate in each sentence below.

5. My best friend worked on the science project with me.

6. Her mother and my father and brother offered to help us with the project.

7. We wanted to do it on our own.

8. They were proud of us for winning second place!

Apply Write a paragraph describing a time when you, or someone you know, competed for a prize or an honor. Make sure you use complete sentences.

_____

_____

_____

_____

_____

_____

_____

_____

_____

Words into Syllables

Focus Sometimes it is helpful to break words into syllables to spell and pronounce them correctly.

> • When the vowel sound in the syllable is short, usually the word is divided after the consonant that follows the short vowel sound. For example, in the word *interview*, the vowel sound in the first syllable is short, so the word is divided after the next consonant, the *n* (in•ter•view).
>
> • Sometimes words can be broken into syllables between double consonants (snap•ping).

Practice Write each word with a line between the syllables.

1. funnel _____

2. clipper _____

3. bedrock _____

4. pastime _____

5. dribble _____

6. medley _____

7. trigger _____

8. compact _____

9. enslave _____

10. smuggler _____

11. expect _____

12. subject _____

Choose the word from each pair that has all syllables ending in a consonant sound. Rewrite the word, drawing a line between the syllables.

13. penmanship   protrude   _____

14. species   sudden   _____

15. biscuit   beeline   _____

16. favorite   falcon   _____

17. deliver   dishpan   _____

18. content   community   _____

19. bicycle   basket   _____

20. lesson   reliable   _____

Apply List three more words that have syllables ending in a consonant sound. Write a sentence using each word.

_____

_____

_____

_____

_____

_____

_____

_____

_____

_____

_____

_____

Name _____ Date _____

Commas in Direct Address

Focus Use commas to set apart words of direct address in sentences. The correct use of commas helps to make writing clear to readers.

> If a speaker addresses someone by name, use a comma to separate the name from the rest of the sentence.
>
> - If the name is at the beginning of a sentence, a comma comes after it.
>   Ed, don't you want to win?
>
> - If the name is at the end of a sentence, a comma comes before it.
>   Do you think winning is most important, Mr. Tillman?
>
> - If the name is in the middle of a sentence, a comma comes before and after it.
>   Listen here, John, I don't care if we lose.

Identify Look through "S.O.R. Losers" for examples of dialogue in which the name of the person who is being spoken to is part of a sentence. Write the page number, the name of the person spoken to, and the sentence. Pay special attention to where the commas are placed.

Page: _____   Person's name: _____

Sentence: _____

_____

_____

Page: _____   Person's name: _____

Sentence: _____

_____

_____

Practice Read the following dialogue. Some of the sentences are missing commas to set apart the names used in direct address. Insert commas where they belong.

"Mr. Tillman isn't it true that you tried out for
pro football?"

"Well, yes Ed, that is true."

"So you lost once, too, Mr. Tillman."

"Yes, Ed I lost. But we don't have time to talk.
We've got a game to play! Okay team let's go out
there and win this time!"

Apply Write a conversation between you and a classmate, using names in direct address. Pay special attention to where commas are placed.

_____

_____

_____

_____

_____

_____

_____

_____

_____

_____

_____

_____

_____

_____

Name _____ Date _____

Cause and Effect

Focus Writers often provide clues that signal cause-
and-effect relationships between events in their stories.

When one event causes another to happen, the events have
a **cause-and-effect relationship**.

- A **cause** is an event that makes it possible for another
  event to happen. An **effect** is the result of another event.

- Clue words such as *because, since, therefore,* and *so* let
  the reader know that there is a cause-and-effect
  relationship between parts of a sentence.

    I was late for school *because* the school bus was late.
    The door was locked, *so* I had to use my key.

Identify Look through "Storks" to find out why the following
events happened. Write down what caused them to take place.

1. The students got out of school early because _____

   _____

2. Lina thought the storks didn't come to Shora because _____

   _____

3. Lina was angry with the boys because _____

   _____

4. The teacher was disappointed with Lina because _____

   _____

5. Some adults thought there were no trees in Shora because _____

   _____

Practice Some of the sentences below show causes, and other sentences show effects. Complete each sentence by adding the missing part of the cause-and-effect relationship.

1. Angelina was covered in flour because _____

_____

2. The music teacher did not show up for class, so _____

_____

3. Nathan left school early because _____

_____

4. Christy suddenly laughed out loud because _____

_____

5. Since it was raining outside, _____

_____

Apply Write a paragraph, using the beginning below. It can be as silly as you like.

I never eat bananas because _____

_____

_____

_____

_____

_____

_____

_____

Author's Point of View

Focus Good writers understand how and when to use
a specific point of view to tell a story.

The **author's point of view** is the position from which
a story is told. Stories are told from either a **first-person**
or a **third-person** point of view.

With a **first-person point of view**, the narrator

- is a character in the story.

- uses the pronouns *I, me, my, we, us,* and *our.*

- reveals only his or her thoughts and feelings.

In the **third-person point of view**, the narrator

- is an outside observer of the story.

- uses the pronouns *he, she, they, him, her,* and *them.*

- reveals thoughts and feelings or reports words and
actions of more than one character.

Identify Look though "Storks" and select a sentence that
contains pronouns that are clues to the author's point of view.

Page: _____

Sentence: _____

_____

Pronouns that are clues to the author's point of view: _____

_____

What person is the selection written in? _____

Practice For each paragraph, write whether the point of view is first person or third person. Underline the pronouns that are clues.

1. My first day of school was awful. First came the spilt pudding incident—anyone who was in the lunchroom can tell you about it. Then came the call to the principal's office.

   Point of view: _____

2. When Ulla first came to Earth, she could not understand why humans lived in houses instead of underground. She soon found out.

   Point of view: _____

3. Any true music fan in Larchmont had to go to the Screaming Furs concert. That's why I was so desperate for a ticket. However, when I got to the ticket booth, the concert was already sold out.

   Point of view: _____

Apply Rewrite one of the above paragraphs from another point of view. Continue the story, if you want to.

_____

_____

_____

_____

_____

_____

_____

_____

_____

Literary Terms: Title, Author, Illustrator

Storks

Focus When a story is created, there are some important people involved and some key elements the story must have.

- A **title** is the name an author gives a story, play, or poem. Often, the title gives readers information on what they are about to read.

- An **author** is a person who creates any piece of literature, including fiction, nonfiction, plays, and poetry. An author who writes
  - plays is called a **playwright.**
  - poetry is called a **poet.**

- An **illustrator** is a person who creates the art that is shown with a piece of writing. An illustrator might draw, paint, or make a collage. Sometimes photographs are used instead of illustrations. The person who takes them is called a **photographer**.

Identify Answer the following questions about a selection of your choice in this unit.

1. What is the title of the selection?

   _____

2. What is the author's name? _____

3. What is the illustrator's name? _____

4. Do the illustrations add to your understanding of the story, or do they take away from it? Explain your answer.

   _____

   _____

   _____

Practice Pick two of your favorite books, stories, or poems.
Write their titles, authors, and illustrators. Then write down
what each title tells you about the piece of writing.

_____

_____

_____

_____

_____

_____

Apply Write a paragraph about what you think might happen
if the storks come back to Shora. Make up a title and write
your name as the author. If you choose to create a picture to
go with your story, do so and add your name as the illustrator.

_____

_____

_____

_____

_____

_____

_____

_____

_____

_____

Capitalizing Titles

Focus Titles of books, magazines, movies, plays, stories, reports, poems, and songs are capitalized.

- Capitalize the first, last, and any important words in a title.
- Capitalize the first word after a colon in a title.
- Capitalize people's names in a title.
- Articles (*a, an, the*), short conjunctions (*but, and*), and short prepositions (*of, to*) in titles are not capitalized unless they are the first or last word.

Practice Identify the titles in the following sentences. Then, rewrite the sentences, correctly capitalizing the titles. If the title is in italics, underline it when you write it.

1. *A wrinkle in time* is my favorite book.

_____

_____

2. I like the poem "every time i climb a tree."

_____

_____

3. I enjoyed reading *bridge to terabithia*.

_____

_____

4. I think *star wars* is the best movie I have ever seen.

_____

_____

5. If you are interested in airplanes, read Russell Freedman's book entitled *the wright brothers: how they invented the airplane.*

_____

_____

_____

_____

Apply Read the following letter a student wrote to a friend. Correctly capitalize the titles in the letter.

Dear Alan,

    We have been studying mythology for the past two weeks. We read the book entitled *myths and legends from around the world.* It had some great stories in it. My favorite story was "King Arthur's Round Table." I think there is a movie out about King Arthur, based on a book called *merlin.* Maybe we could see the movie sometime. Hope to hear from you soon.

                Your friend,

                Marcos

Drawing Conclusions

Galileo

Focus When writers don't include all the information about a character or event in their story, good readers draw conclusions using information in the text.

Drawing conclusions means putting together information from the text to make a statement about a character or event. The conclusion won't be stated directly, but should be supported by information in the text.

Identify Look through "Galileo." What conclusions did you come to about people or events in the selection? Find places in the text that helped you to draw conclusions.

Page: _____

Conclusion: _____

Information that supports the conclusion: _____

_____

_____

_____

_____

Page: _____

Conclusion: _____

Information that supports the conclusion: _____

_____

_____

_____

Practice Think about an important space discovery that you might want a reader to draw a conclusion about. It could be in the past, or it could be a more recent discovery. First, decide what conclusion you want the reader to draw. Then, write some clues that will help the reader come to that conclusion.

The discovery: _____

Conclusion: _____

Clues: _____

_____

_____

_____

Apply Use the above clues to write a paragraph about the discovery you chose. Read your paragraph to a classmate and have him or her draw a conclusion about the discovery. Discuss what information in the paragraph the conclusion was based on.

_____

_____

_____

_____

_____

_____

_____

_____

_____

Recognizing a Biography

Focus A biography is a story of a real person's life that is written by another person.

A **biography**

- is a type of nonfiction that tells about a person's entire life or about an important part or event in a person's life.

- is written by someone other than its subject and is usually written from the third-person point of view.
  The Life and Times of George Washington by N. Mac

An **autobiography**

- is a type of nonfiction that tells the story of a real person's life and is written by that person.

- is usually written from the first-person point of view.
  My Life: How I Learned the Secret to Happiness by Jason Thomas

---

Identify Biographies often tell us about events in a person's life and about the times in which a person lived. Look through "Galileo" and answer the following questions.

1. Does this biography tell about Galileo's entire life, an important part of his life, or one key event in his life? Explain.

_____

_____

_____

2. What does this biography tell us about the times in which Galileo lived?

_____

_____

Practice Read each of the following book titles. Write the correct letter or letters beside each title. Write *B* for biography, *A* for autobiography, *F* for fiction, and *N* for nonfiction.

1. *My Life as an Astronaut* _____

2. *Batman and Robin Save the Day* _____

3. *Building the Tree House of Your Dreams* _____

4. *The United States During World War II* _____

5. *Benjamin Franklin: America's Great Inventor* _____

6. *Escape from the Haunted Island* _____

7. *Gardening Made Easy* _____

8. *The Life and Times of Andrew Jackson* _____

Apply Write a short biography of someone you know. Either tell about one specific event or give a brief history of the person's life.

_____

_____

_____

_____

_____

_____

_____

_____

_____

_____

_____

Content-Area Words

Galileo

Focus Good readers know that the meaning of a word may depend on the content area, or subject, in which it is being used.

To understand the meaning of a word with multiple meanings, note

- the subject area in which the word is encountered.
- the context in which the word is being used in a sentence.

For example, the word *volume* has different meanings.

Subject Area	Context Sentence	Meaning
math	What is the volume of this box?	amount of space occupied by a three-dimensional object
science	Turn up the volume on the radio.	loudness of sound
language arts	What volume of the book do you need?	printed sheets bound together to make a book

Identify Read the following sentences from "Galileo." Determine the meaning of the underlined words and write a sentence using each of them in a different context.

1. "He saw that it was a small round <u>disk</u> that did not sparkle like a star."

   Different context: _____

   _____

2. "Galileo had opened up a new <u>vision</u> of the heavens."

   Different context: _____

   _____

Practice Write a mathematical meaning for each of these words. If you need help, use a dictionary.

1. diameter: _____

_____

_____

2. axis: _____

_____

_____

3. angle: _____

_____

_____

Apply Write a sentence for each of the following words from "Galileo," but use a meaning that is in a content area other than astronomy.

1. boundary: _____

_____

_____

2. distance: _____

_____

_____

3. deduction: _____

_____

_____

Main Idea and Details

Focus Writers make their ideas clear by organizing them into paragraphs.

- The **main idea** is what a paragraph is mostly about. Writers often place the main idea in a topic sentence at the beginning or the end of a paragraph.

- The other sentences in a paragraph provide **details**, or more information, that support the main idea.

Identify Look back at "Telescopes." Identify a paragraph with a main idea stated in a topic sentence. Write the page number, the main idea, and a detail from the paragraph that supports the main idea.

Page: _____   Main idea in topic sentence: _____

_____

_____

_____

_____

Detail that supports the main idea: _____

_____

_____

_____

_____

_____

_____

Practice Rewrite the following passage, beginning a new paragraph whenever a new main idea is introduced.

The last day of school is always sad for me. I remember the good times I have had with my friends and the exciting things we have done in class. I wish school would go on all summer long. Don't get me wrong; I like summer, too. And after a few days, I get over being sad and start enjoying my vacation. I especially enjoy not having to get up early. Last summer, we had an exchange student from Italy stay with us. He taught me how to speak a few words of Italian and helped Mom and Dad cook some fabulous Italian meals.

_____

_____

_____

_____

_____

_____

_____

_____

_____

_____

_____

Apply Look through several newspaper or magazine articles. Choose a paragraph where the main idea is stated in the first sentence. Choose another paragraph where the main idea is stated in the last sentence. Clip the articles you selected and underline the main idea in each paragraph.

Features of Informational Text

Focus A good writer of informational text presents facts in a way that is informative, interesting, and well organized.

Informational text

- is nonfiction.
- has a main topic.
- contains subtopics that relate to the main topic.
- explains several facts about each subtopic.
- sometimes contains charts, tables, and diagrams.

Identify Look through "Telescopes" and write an *X* next to the features of informational text that it includes.

_____	main topic	_____	explanation of technical terms
_____	subtopics	_____	facts about each subtopic
_____	footnotes	_____	glossary
_____	tables, charts, or diagrams	_____	bibliography
_____	index	_____	table of contents
_____	nonfiction	_____	photographs

Practice Read the following informational text and complete the outline.

Small Moving Objects in Our Solar System

If you study the night sky for a month, you can see planets like Mars and Saturn creep about. Some small objects, such as comets or meteoroids, streak across the sky in a matter of days or even moments.

A comet is a lump of ice and dust that revolves around the sun in a very large orbit. It can be seen from Earth when its orbit comes close to the sun. As it heats up, it releases gas and dust, which are seen as a streak in the sky.

A meteoroid is a chunk of stone or metal that plunges into our atmosphere at high speed. When it enters Earth's atmosphere, it heats up and is seen as a "falling star." A meteoroid that falls to Earth is called a meteorite.

Title: _____

Main Topic: _____

A. Subtopic 1: _____

    Fact 1: _____

    Fact 2: _____

    _____

B. Subtopic 2: _____

    Fact 1: _____

    Fact 2: _____

    _____

Apply On a sheet of paper, write informational text that describes how an object, such as a bicycle or camera, works. Remember to include a main topic, subtopics, and facts about each subtopic. You may also choose to include a diagram.

Making Inferences

Focus Good readers can make inferences about a character or event in a story.

> Making inferences is using information from the text, along with one's own experiences or knowledge, to
> - get a fuller understanding of story characters.
> - figure out a more complete picture of story events.

Identify Make an inference about each of the following characters from "The Heavenly Zoo." Then, write down the examples from the story that helped you make the inference.

Orion: _____

_____

Examples: _____

_____

Yudistira: _____

_____

Examples: _____

_____

Arjuna: _____

_____

Examples: _____

_____

Making Inferences *(continued)*

Practice Prepare to write a paragraph that will leave out information for the reader to infer. First, choose a famous person and write down his or her name. Then, list some characteristics or other information about the person.

Famous person: _____

Characteristics or other information: _____

_____

_____

_____

Apply Now, use your notes to write a paragraph about the person you chose. Do not use the person's name in your paragraph. Show your paragraph to a classmate to see if he or she can infer from your paragraph who the person is.

_____

_____

_____

_____

_____

_____

_____

_____

_____

_____

_____

_____

Recognizing Myths

Focus Myths are stories that have been told for centuries in cultures all around the world. Because they were originally told by word of mouth, different versions of myths appear in written form.

Myths

- often explain something about nature.
- suggest mystical reasons for why natural events occur.
- feature main characters who have a special gift or skill.

Identify Look through the two stories in "The Heavenly Zoo." Write down details from each story that indicate the stories are both myths.

Details from "The Great Dog": _____

_____

_____

_____

_____

Details from "The Scorpion": _____

_____

_____

_____

_____

Practice After each story description, explain why each story
is a myth.

1. Baal, the creator of storms, uses his mace to make thunder.
   Then, with his lance, he creates lightning, which flashes
   across the sky.

   _____

   _____

   _____

2. Demeter, the ruler of growing things, is sad when her daughter
   Persephone goes to live for four months of every year with
   Hades, ruler of the underworld. As a result, she allows nothing
   to grow during the time each year that her daughter is gone.
   This story is an explanation for why there are seasons.

   _____

   _____

   _____

Apply Read a myth that you've checked out from your school
or local library. Write the name of the story, then explain why
the story is a myth.

Title of story: _____

Explanation: _____

_____

_____

_____

_____

_____

Developing Vocabulary by Listening

Focus Writers can develop their vocabularies by listening carefully for unfamiliar words.

When you hear an unfamiliar word,

- write the word.
- listen for familiar word parts that could provide clues about the meaning of the word.
- listen for other sentences that include the word to help make the meaning clear.
- think about what the definition might be.
- discuss the word with another person.
- look up the word in a dictionary later.

Practice With a partner, read aloud each sentence below. Discuss the meaning of the underlined word and circle the clue word or words in the sentence that help to explain its meaning.

1. The hero was <u>weary</u> after the long, tiring travel home.

2. Yudistira's brothers were all <u>summoned</u>, or called away, from their journey.

3. Svana was Yudistira's true friend and <u>companion</u>, because he stayed with Yudistira for the entire journey.

4. Orion was asked to live with the gods instead of <u>dwelling</u> in the Underworld.

5. He was <u>seized</u> with love and captured by her beauty.

Apply Write a story that explains how the Big Dipper (or the Great Bear) was created. Include some of the vocabulary words you learned from "The Heavenly Zoo."

_____

_____

_____

_____

_____

_____

_____

_____

_____

_____

_____

_____

_____

_____

_____

_____

_____

_____

_____

_____

Forming the Present Tense of Regular and Irregular Verbs

Focus Writers must check the use and spelling of regular and irregular verbs.

Here are some rules for forming the present tense of regular verbs.

- If the subject is singular (except *I* or *you*), add *-s* or *-es* to verbs to form the present tense.

•For most verbs, add *-s* to the end of the verb.
•For verbs that end with *-ch*, *-sh*, *-s*, *-ss*, *-x*, or *-z*, add *-es*.
•For verbs that end with a consonant followed by *y*, change the *y* to *i* and add *-es*.

- If the subject is plural, or if the subject is *I* or *you*, **do not** add an ending to verbs to form the present tense.

Irregular verbs have special present-tense forms that you must remember.

be	I am. You are. He is. She is. It is. We are. They are.
do	I do. You do. He does. She does. It does. We do. They do.
have	I have. You have. He has. She has. It has. We have. They have.

Practice Underline the correct present-tense forms for the subjects below.

1. The cheerleader (rally, rallies) the crowd.

2. I (do, does) math homework every night.

3. My brother and I (catch, catches) the bus to the mall.

4. Learning new words (motivate, motivates) me to read a lot.

5. There (is, are) 50 computers in our school.

Forming the Present Tense of Regular and Irregular Verbs *(continued)*

Rewrite each of these sentences in the present tense.

6. We planned to meet at the movie theater.

_____

7. Playing basketball was her favorite sport.

_____

8. Our dog buried his bone in the backyard.

_____

9. The customer tapped on the store window.

_____

10. All of the Jones children had the same Spanish teacher.

_____

Apply Write a paragraph describing something that is happening to you or someone else right now. Use as many present-tense regular and irregular verbs as you can.

_____

_____

_____

_____

_____

_____

_____

_____

_____

Classify and Categorize

Focus Readers sometimes classify characters, items, or events and put them into categories to help organize their thoughts and to help them remember similar things.

- To **classify** means to put similar things together into a group, or category.
- A **category** is the actual group similar things are put into.
- Things can often fit into more than one category.

Identify Look through "Circles, Squares, and Daggers" for information on the following classifications. Complete the chart by giving each category, or group, an appropriate heading.

Aldebaran Rigel Sirius Fomalhaut	Ponca Mississippian Anasazi

Classify and Categorize *(continued)*

Practice Read the following list and classify the items into categories. Write both headings and items.

Voyager	Orion	Uranus	Neptune
Saturn	*Magellan*	Centauri	*Viking*
Andromeda			

Apply Review the three categories you identified above. Think about how each category could be classified differently, for example, by specific physical features, by distance, or by meanings. Write down your ideas below.

Category 1: _____

Item 1: _____ Item 2: _____ Item 3: _____

Category 2: _____

Item 1: _____ Item 2: _____ Item 3: _____

Category 3: _____

Item 1: _____ Item 2: _____ Item 3: _____

Compare and Contrast

Focus Writers often use comparison and contrast to help readers understand ideas.

To **compare** means to tell how two or more things are similar, or alike. Some words that signal comparison are *both*, *like*, *as*, *also*, *too*, and *neither . . . nor*.

To **contrast** means to tell how two or more things are different. Some words that signal contrast are *different*, *instead of*, *but*, *rather than*, and *unlike*.

Practice Underline the clue word in each sentence. Then tell whether the things are being compared or contrasted.

1. Jane enjoys sports, but her twin brother, John, prefers computers.

   _____

2. Like Mr. Zebra last year, our teacher this year, Mr. Wells, does not allow us to chew gum.

   _____

3. Unlike goldfish that need cold water, tropical fish must have warm water to survive.

   _____

4. Both the pianist and the violinist were late for the concert.

   _____

5. I'd like a scrambled egg instead of a fried egg.

   _____

6. Rather than going to a play, let's see a movie.

   _____

Compare and Contrast (*continued*)

Combine each pair of sentences into one sentence that compares or contrasts. Use clue words to make the meaning clear.

7. Cars are not allowed in the park. Bicycles are allowed in the park.

_____

_____

8. The dolphins put on an excellent performance. The seals forgot their tricks.

_____

_____

9. My family loves dogs. Max's family loves dogs.

_____

_____

10. Henry doesn't know how to swim. His younger sister doesn't know how to swim.

_____

_____

Apply Write a sentence comparing two movies that you've seen or two songs that you've heard. Then, write a sentence contrasting them.

1. Comparison: _____

_____

_____

2. Contrast: _____

_____

_____

Subject and Verb Agreement

Focus The subject and verb of a sentence must agree. Understanding subject and verb agreement and using correct verb forms are important when writing.

- A subject and verb must agree in number. A singular subject takes a singular verb; a plural subject takes a plural verb.

- The words *anyone, everyone, somebody, either,* and *each* take a singular verb.

- Two subjects connected with the word *and* take a plural verb.

- Two singular subjects connected by *or* or *nor* take a singular verb.

Practice In each sentence, underline the subject and circle the verb that agrees with it.

1. The boys in my class (play, plays) video games after school.

2. The computers (is, are) turned off at the end of the day.

3. Terry and Leslie (is, are) twins.

4. Sometimes my sister (wash, washes) my hair for me.

5. Mr. Carlino and his children (visit, visits) the art museum each Sunday.

6. Teresa (want, wants) to be in the marching band.

7. Did the boys (take, takes) the soccer ball outside?

8. Everyone (like, likes) to celebrate birthdays.

Subject and Verb Agreement *(continued)*

Fill in each blank with the correct form of the verb shown in parentheses at the end of the sentence.

9. Everyone in my class _____ to sports practice after school. (go)

10. Neither my CD player nor my cassette player _____ working. (be)

11. The radio and the television _____ on at the same time. (be)

12. Mr. Smith and his students _____ working together. (enjoy)

13. The corn with the white kernels _____ in this field. (grow)

14. Father's head _____ the ceiling in the basement. (touch)

15. One of the books _____ torn pages. (have)

Apply Write a sentence using each verb or subject in parentheses. Be sure that your subjects and verbs agree.

1. (reaches) _____

   _____

2. (Mom and Dad) _____

   _____

3. (somebody) _____

   _____

4. (has) _____

   _____

5. (do) _____

   _____

Classify and Categorize

Focus When readers put things or ideas into groups based on shared characteristics, it helps them organize their thoughts and remember the different kinds of details in a story.

> - **Classify** means to put similar things together into a group, or category.
>
> - **Categories** are the actual groups that similar things are put into.
>
> - Objects, characters, and events can often fit into more than one category.
>
> - A broad category can often be further classified into a more specific category.

Identify Look through the first two pages of "Stars" and list five classifications of heavenly bodies found in the sky.

1. _____

2. _____

3. _____

4. _____

5. _____

Classify and Categorize *(continued)*

Practice and Apply On the diagram below, heavenly bodies have been broadly classified into stars, planets, and constellations. Think of ways to make these broad categories more specific. Then, complete the diagram.

	Stars	a.
		b.
		c.
HEAVENLY BODIES	**Planets**	a.
		b.
		c.
	Constellations	a.
		b.
		c.

Name _____   Date _____

Authors Organize
Information in Specific Ways

Focus Good writers try to organize their information in a way that best communicates their ideas. They also want their writing to be interesting and easy to understand.

Here are some ways you might organize information.

- Make a statement that contains the main idea at the beginning of a paragraph. Then, use the body of the paragraph to explain or provide examples.

- Begin a paragraph with examples and explanations. Then, sum them up at the end of a paragraph with a statement that contains the main idea.

Practice Prepare to write an informational paragraph on what you find interesting about stars. Use one of the ways to organize information described above. Use the lines below to plan your paragraph.

_____

_____

_____

_____

_____

_____

_____

_____

_____

Apply Write your paragraph, using your plan on the previous
page to help you.

_____

_____

_____

_____

_____

_____

_____

_____

_____

_____

_____

_____

_____

_____

_____

_____

_____

_____

Content-Area Words

Focus A word you use in everyday conversation may have a different meaning in a specific content area.

A **content area** can be

- a subject area, such as math, science, social studies, art, or language arts.

- a field or area of study, such as education, finance, law, family, or religion.

- an industry, such as technology, entertainment, banking, or sports.

Identify Below are some familiar science-related words from "Stars." Use context clues in the story to help you write science-related meanings for the words. Then, write a different meaning for each word.

Word	Science-Related Meaning	Alternate Meaning
1. banded		
2. bright		
3. nature		
4. gas		

Practice Select a word from the box to complete each sentence. Use clues in the sentence to help you figure out the correct word.

magnified	astronomical	frequency	concave

1. Many signals were registering on the computer. The high

   _____ of the signals helped the scientists determine the location of the star.

2. An _____ telescope is used to view far-off planets, stars, and galaxies.

3. A _____ mirror is one that curves inward like the inside of a bowl.

4. When students looked through the telescope, the stars looked much closer because they were

   _____ .

Apply Write a paragraph explaining what you learned about the different kinds of telescopes. Include in your paragraph some of the science-related words from the selection.

_____

_____

_____

_____

_____

_____

_____

_____

Name _____ Date _____

Main Idea and Details

Focus Writers need to organize their ideas carefully.

The **main idea** is what the text is about.

- A main idea should be clear and focused.
- A main idea should have supporting details.

Details support the main idea and provide additional
information about it.

Identify Look through "The Book That Saved the Earth" and
complete the following.

What is the main idea of the entire story?

_____

_____

Write three detail sentences that support the main idea.

Sentence 1:

_____

_____

Sentence 2:

_____

_____

Sentence 3:

_____

_____

Practice and Apply Write a paragraph using the two sentences provided below. Use detail sentences for each paragraph that clearly present your ideas.

Sentence 1: **A book can be a lifesaver when you least expect it.**

_____

_____

_____

_____

_____

_____

_____

_____

Sentence 2: **The most important book that I have**

      ever read is _____.

_____

_____

_____

_____

_____

_____

_____

Developing Vocabulary by Listening

Focus Writers and readers can develop their vocabularies by listening carefully for unfamiliar words.

When you hear an unfamiliar word,

- write the word.
- listen for familiar words that could provide clues about the meaning of the word.
- listen for other sentences that include the word to help make the meaning clear.
- think about what the definition might be.
- discuss the word with another person.
- look up the word in a dictionary later.

Identify Look through "The Book That Saved the Earth" for examples of unfamiliar words. Write the unfamiliar word and the definition on the lines below.

Page: _____   Unfamiliar word: _____

Definition: _____

Page: _____   Unfamiliar word: _____

Definition: _____

Developing Vocabulary by Listening *(continued)*

Practice and Apply Listen to an informational TV program.
Select two words that are unfamiliar to you. Use the steps
listed in the box on the previous page. Write your notes on the
lines below. Then, write a sentence using each word correctly.

_____

_____

_____

_____

_____

_____

_____

_____

_____

_____

_____

_____

_____

_____

_____

_____

_____

Commas in a Series

Focus Writers use commas to separate a series of three or more nouns, adjectives, verbs, or phrases in a sentence.

> In a series of three or more nouns, adjectives, verbs, or phrases, place a comma after each word or phrase that comes before the conjunction *and* or *or*.
>
> Our teacher will play the flute, the clarinet, or the piano.
>
> Eve is a smart, patient, and dedicated student of music.
>
> Every day we work, play, and rest.
>
> The audience walked through the door, into the theater, and down the aisle.

Practice Write *correct* for each sentence in which commas are used correctly. Rewrite and correct sentences in which commas are not used correctly.

1. My canary sings, chirps, and squawks all day long.

_____

_____

2. Your keys are in the drawer, on the table or next to the television.

_____

_____

3. The pet store has a fine selection of dogs, cats, gerbils, and birds.

_____

_____

4. Jeff asked, begged, and pleaded for a new bike.

_____

_____

5. At camp, we went swimming in the lake at the cove
and in the pool.

_____

_____

6. The small, ugly, furry caterpillar eventually turns into a
beautiful butterfly.

_____

_____

7. At the zoo we saw monkeys tigers, and elephants.

_____

_____

8. To get to work each morning, Mr. Williams can drive a car,
take a bus, or walk.

_____

_____

Apply Write a sentence on the topic below using commas
correctly.

three or more subjects you study in school

_____

_____

_____

Author's Purpose

Focus Writers have a purpose in mind when they write a selection.

An author's purpose, or reason for writing a selection, can be
- to inform.
- to explain.
- to persuade.
- to entertain.

Identify Look through "The Land I Lost" and complete the following. What was the author's purpose for writing this story? Give examples from the story that support your opinion.

Author's purpose: _____

_____

Page: _____

Example: _____

_____

_____

_____

Page: _____

Example: _____

_____

_____

_____

Practice Read the paragraphs below and write the author's purpose for each one.

To grow tomatoes, first plant seeds in soil in small starter pots. Water the pots and set them in a sunny place. Within a few days, you should see the seedlings coming up. Be sure to keep the soil moist. When the seedlings are about a foot high, plant them outside. Water them immediately.

Author's purpose: _____

Tomatoes are one of the most popular items in the fresh produce section of the grocery store. Although most people think tomatoes are vegetables, they are actually fruits. In the early 1500s, tomatoes were called "love apples" and thought to be poisonous.

Author's purpose: _____

Apply Write a paragraph about a person in history. Decide whether this paragraph will inform, explain, persuade, or entertain. Write its purpose. Then, write the paragraph.

_____

_____

_____

_____

_____

_____

_____

_____

Recognizing Autobiography

The Land I Lost

Focus An **autobiography** is the true story of a person's life. It is written by a person about his or her own life.

An **autobiography**

- allows the reader to learn a lot about the person.
- allows the writer to share his or her feelings and life experiences with others.
- allows the writer to share what it was like to live in a certain place and during a certain time.

Identify Look through "The Land I Lost: Adventures of a Boy in Vietnam" for the following information.

1. What parts of the title are clues that this story is an autobiography?

   _____

   _____

2. What does Huynh give the most details about on the first two pages of the story? What are his feelings toward what he describes?

   _____

   _____

   _____

3. What person, other than Huynh, is the rest of the story mainly about, and how did Huynh feel about the person?

   _____

   _____

Recognizing Autobiography (continued)

Practice Read each pair of book titles. Underline the titles that are likely to be autobiographies.

1. *How the West Was Won*   *How I Helped Tame the West*

2. *My Life As a Clown*   *Clowns in the Circus of Life*

3. *The Way I See It: My Ideas on Education*   *The Opinions of Two Scholars*

4. *Memories of a Globetrotter*   *The Day the Globetrotters Came to Town*

5. *The Land Beyond the Mountains*   *My Life Beyond the Mountains*

Apply Write an autobiographical paragraph about an important event, experience, or time in your life.

_____

_____

_____

_____

_____

_____

_____

_____

_____

_____

_____

_____

_____

Syllable Boundary Patterns

The Land I Lost

Focus **Syllable boundary patterns** are rules for dividing a word into word parts, or syllables, that help readers pronounce, spell, or write a word correctly.

- Some words that contain two consonants between two vowels can be divided between the two consonants.

    ham•mer

- Some words that contain three consonants between two vowels can be divided between the consonant and the consonant blend.

    ram•bling

Identify Look through "The Land I Lost: Adventures of a Boy in Vietnam" and write words with each spelling pattern described above.

Two Consonants Between Two Vowels	Three Consonants Between Two Vowels

Syllable Boundary Patterns (continued)

Practice Use what you know about syllable boundary patterns to rewrite the following words with a line between the syllables.

1. stammer _____

2. rapture _____

3. sandwich _____

4. basket _____

5. lobster _____

Apply Write a sentence that contains words that fit each description below. Underline the words that show the spelling patterns described.

1. Two words with two consonants between two vowels:

   _____

   _____

   _____

2. Two words with three consonants between two vowels:

   _____

   _____

   _____

3. One word with two consonants between two vowels and one word with three consonants between two vowels:

   _____

   _____

   _____

Pronoun Referents

Focus Knowing how to make pronouns agree with the nouns they refer to can make your writing clearer and more accurate.

A **pronoun** is a word that takes the place of and refers to a noun. The noun is the **antecedent** or **referent** that the pronoun replaces. A pronoun must agree in number, gender, and person with its antecedent.

- Use singular pronouns to replace singular nouns.

- Use plural pronouns to replace plural nouns.

- Use subject pronouns to replace nouns used as subjects.
  <u>Byron</u> ran the marathon. <u>He</u> won the race.

- Use object pronouns to replace nouns used as objects.
  Byron told his <u>friends</u> that he won. He told <u>them</u> on Saturday.

- Use possessive pronouns to replace possessive nouns.
  <u>Byron's</u> friends were happy. <u>His</u> friends were also surprised.

Practice Read each sentence. Write a pronoun that can replace the underlined word or words.

1. <u>Martin</u> no longer goes to this school. _____

2. Last week I fixed <u>the computer's</u> disk drive. _____

3. This bike belongs to <u>Harry and Michelle Jones.</u> _____

4. Did <u>Betsy</u> say she was going to attend the meeting? _____

5. The presents are for <u>Allen and me.</u> _____

6. Maybe <u>the flowers</u> will last until Sunday. _____

Write the correct pronoun in each blank to complete each sentence or pair of sentences.

7. <u>Mario's</u> bike is new. _____ bike is quite expensive.

8. The <u>car</u> has a dent on _____ rear fender.

9. <u>Maggie</u> is a police officer. _____ graduated from the police academy last week.

10. Ali called her <u>cousins</u> on the phone. She told _____ to meet her at the mall at noon.

Apply Rewrite the following paragraphs, replacing the underlined word or words with the correct pronouns.

    Margaret works in a day care center. <u>Margaret</u> takes care of four-year-olds. <u>Margaret</u> thinks <u>four-year-olds</u> are lots of fun. Last week one of <u>the four-year-olds</u> made a car out of clay. Margaret didn't think <u>the clay</u> looked much like a car, but four-year-old Michael did.

    "Look," said Michael. "Here's <u>the car's</u> steering wheel, and these are the tires." Then <u>Michael</u> picked up <u>Michael's</u> clay car and changed <u>the clay car</u> into a pancake!

_____

_____

_____

_____

_____

_____

_____

_____

Name _____ Date _____

Compare and Contrast

Focus Writers compare and contrast to paint a clearer picture of the people and things they are writing about.

> • To **compare** means to tell how things, events, or characters are similar, or alike.
>
> • To **contrast** means to tell how things, events, or characters are different.

Identify Look through "In Two Worlds" and find contrasts between the Scammon Bay of Mary Ann's childhood and the Scammon Bay of today. What things have changed?

1. In Mary Ann's time: _____

_____

_____

Today: _____

_____

_____

2. In Mary Ann's time: _____

_____

_____

Today: _____

_____

_____

Compare and Contrast (*continued*)

Practice Read each sentence and tell whether it shows a comparison or a contrast. Then, rewrite each sentence the other way. Note the change that occurs in the meaning.

1. Dave and Edmund both finished all their vegetables. _____

_____

_____

2. Marta plays the trombone, while Janet plays the cello. _____

_____

3. I like to read mysteries just like my sister Gina. _____

_____

_____

4. Both cats and dogs make good pets. _____

_____

5. Jacob and Jason are twins, but Jacob is slightly taller. _____

_____

_____

Apply Write a paragraph comparing and contrasting yourself to a friend or relative. Be sure to include ways that you are similar and ways that you are different.

_____

_____

_____

_____

_____

_____

Compare and Contrast • **Reading and Writing Workbook**

Use a Dictionary to Clarify Meaning and Usage

Focus Dictionaries are useful to both writers and readers.

The main parts of a dictionary are

- the **entry word**, which appears in alphabetical order and is usually in dark type. It shows how the word is spelled and how it can be divided in writing.

- the **guide words**, which appear at the top of each page and are usually in dark type. The word on the left indicates the first entry word listed on the page, while the word on the right indicates the last entry word listed on the page.

- the **pronunciation**, which follows the entry word and usually appears in parentheses.

- the **part-of-speech label**, which usually follows the pronunciation. It is usually an abbreviation (such as *n.* for *noun*, *v.* for *verb*) and appears in italic type.

- the **definition**, which usually follows the part of speech and tells what the word means. If a word has more than one meaning, the definitions will be numbered.

Identify Use a dictionary to look up the following words from "In Two Worlds" and complete the chart below.

Entry Word	Pronunciation	Part of Speech	Definition
tundra			
harpoon			
precarious			

Practice Find and write the definition for each of the following words. Then, use each word in a sentence.

1. inhabit: _____

_____

_____

_____

2. monument: _____

_____

_____

_____

3. enormous: _____

_____

_____

_____

Apply Choose one of the following words that have several different meanings. Find and write at least two different definitions for the word you chose. Then, write a sentence for each meaning of the word.

present	counter	lead

_____

_____

_____

_____

_____

Forming the Present Tense of Verbs

Focus Writers use present tense verbs to describe an action that is happening now or is ongoing.

> The present tense is formed by adding -*s* or -*es* to a verb, except in the case of irregular verbs, such as *be*, *have*, and *do*, which have special present tense forms.
>
> - If the subject of the sentence is singular (except *I* or *you*), add -*s* or -*es* to regular verbs to form the present tense.
> - If the subject is plural, or if the subject is *I* or *you*, do not add an ending to regular verbs to form the present tense.
> - In addition, remember that the verb of a sentence must agree with the subject. If the subject is singular, the verb must be singular. If the subject is plural, the verb must be plural.
>
> | **Singular Subjects and Verbs** | **Plural Subjects and Verbs** |
> |---|---|
> | *I* call, watch, am | *we* call, watch, are |
> | *you* call, watch, are | *you* call, watch, are |
> | *he, she,* or *it* calls, watches, is | *they* call, watch, are |

Practice Write the present tense form of the underlined verb in each sentence.

1. Mrs. Jones <u>decided</u> to end class early. _____

2. We <u>traveled</u> to school by bus. _____

3. Father <u>wished</u> he could take a train to work. _____

4. They <u>did</u> the laundry every Saturday. _____

5. I <u>had</u> math homework. _____

6. We <u>raked</u> the yard in one hour. _____

7. They <u>stopped</u> to eat at a restaurant. _____

Forming the Present Tense of Regular and Irregular Verbs (continued)

Write sentences using the present tense forms of the following verbs. Make sure you use some singular and some plural subjects.

8. search: _____

_____

9. am: _____

_____

10. bounce: _____

_____

11. identify: _____

_____

12. change: _____

_____

Apply Imagine that you are doing some exciting activity, such as running a race, riding a roller coaster, or some other activity. Write a paragraph describing your actions. Use some regular and some irregular verbs in the present tense.

_____

_____

_____

_____

_____

_____

_____

Name _____   Date _____

Regular and Irregular Plurals

Focus Good writers spell plural nouns correctly.

A **plural noun** names two or more people, places, or things.

Forming regular plurals

- Many nouns are made plural by adding -*s*.
    one light, three lights
- Other nouns are made plural by adding an -*s* or -*es*, sometimes after a spelling change to the word.

    For nouns ending in -*y* following a consonant, change the *y* to *i* and add -*es*.
    candy, candies

    For nouns ending in -*s*, -*ss*, -*sh*, -*ch*, -*x*, *or* -*z*, add -*es*.
    bus, buses   lunch, lunches

Forming irregular plurals

- Some nouns are made plural by changing their spellings.
    one goose, two geese
- A few nouns do not change at all in their plural form.
    one deer, two deer

Practice Write the plurals for each of the following nouns.

1. bunch   _____

2. jelly   _____

3. monkey   _____

4. foot   _____

5. sheep   _____

6. mouse   _____

7. cherry   _____

8. class   _____

Regular and Irregular Plurals (*continued*)

Complete each sentence, using one of the words listed below.
Use the plural form of each word.

lunch	baby	box	quiz

9. They stored the holiday decorations in two _____.

10. When the _____ started crying, we all
    hurried to pick them up.

11. The _____ our parents packed tasted
    wonderful.

12. I have math and science _____ every Friday.

Apply Imagine you visited a zoo. Write a paragraph telling
about the different animals you saw. As you write the plurals
of the nouns in your paragraph, be aware of how you are
forming them.

_____

_____

_____

_____

_____

_____

_____

_____

_____

Adverbs

Focus Writers use adverbs to make their writing more
vivid and precise.

Adverbs describe verbs, adjectives, or other adverbs.

- They tell when, where, how, how much, or how often.
  We will arrive <u>soon</u>.

- Many adverbs are formed by adding *-ly* to an adjective.
  Mother walks <u>quietly</u> into the room.

Practice Read the following sentences and circle the adverb
that describes the underlined word in each sentence.

1. Dad sometimes <u>talks</u> about his life as a young boy.

2. The ice cream was melting, so we had to <u>eat</u> it quickly.

3. I will <u>explain</u> it to you later.

4. It was terribly <u>cold</u> the day we went ice-skating.

5. Suddenly the snow <u>fell</u> from the trees.

6. My mom and dad <u>left</u> immediately to go home.

7. We <u>ate</u> our breakfast early.

8. Carol and Kim <u>walked</u> slowly to the bus stop.

9. We easily <u>finished</u> our chores before lunch.

10. Did she <u>open</u> the window carefully?

Adverbs *(continued)*

Complete each sentence using one of the adverbs listed below.

| wickedly | inside | today | loudly | faster |

11. The children had to play _____ because it was raining.

12. The evil troll laughed _____ .

13. The awards were being given _____ in the auditorium.

14. Juan's dog can run _____ than mine.

15. Speak _____ so my grandmother can hear you.

Apply Write a sentence using each adverb below.

1. yesterday: _____

   _____

2. excitedly: _____

   _____

3. quietly: _____

   _____

4. now: _____

   _____

5. frequently: _____

   _____

Name _____   Date _____

Fact and Opinion

Focus Writers may use both facts and opinions in their writing. A good reader can tell one from the other.

- **Facts** are details that can be proven true or false. They provide additional information about main ideas.

- **Opinions** are people's thoughts or feelings about a subject. They can be supported, but cannot be proven true or false.

Identify Look through "Chinatown" for examples of facts and opinions. Write the page numbers and examples below and tell whether each is a fact or an opinion.

Page: _____

Example: _____

_____

_____

Fact or opinion: _____

Page: _____

Example: _____

_____

_____

Fact or opinion: _____

Practice Each of the sentences below states either a fact or an opinion. After each sentence, identify it as *fact* or *opinion*. Then, write a second sentence. If you identified a sentence as a fact, make your sentence an opinion. If you identified a sentence as an opinion, make your sentence a fact.

1. Pizza is the best food. _____

   _____

   _____

2. Almost all of the major rivers in this country flow south. _____

   _____

   _____

3. Country and western music sounds better than most other

   kinds of music. _____

   _____

   _____

Apply Write a paragraph that states your opinion about something. It could be about an issue in your community or school, or some other issue of your choice. Remember that you can use facts to support your opinion.

_____

_____

_____

_____

_____

_____

_____

Name _____   Date _____

Ending Syllables with *-le*

Focus Words that end with the same sound can be spelled in different ways. There are no rules for remembering how to spell such words; they must be studied and memorized individually.

> The consonant before *-le*, *-el*, *-al*, *-il*, and *-ol* are different spellings of the same vowel sound in the unstressed ending syllable of some words. The consonant before *-le* syllable pattern is the most common spelling.

Practice Carefully look at each of the following words. Write *Correct* for each word that is spelled correctly. Correct the ones that are spelled incorrectly.

1. camel   _____
2. fiddel   _____
3. brittle   _____
4. dangil   _____
5. lable   _____
6. triple   _____
7. levle   _____
8. triangel _____
9. plural   _____
10. abel   _____

Ending Syllables with -*le* (*continued*)

Fill in the blanks with a word that ends in the consonant before -*le* syllable pattern. Check the spelling of words you're not sure of in the dictionary.

11. The weight lifter raised his arm to show his bulging _____.

12. The children formed a _____ to play "Ring-Around-the-Rosy."

13. To sew the quilt, I will need a _____ and thread.

14. My grandfather always works the crossword _____ in the daily paper.

15. Millions of _____ visit Washington, D.C. each year.

16. One way to figure out an unknown word is to read each

_____.

Apply Think of four other words that have the consonant before -*le* syllable pattern. Write a sentence using each word.

1. _____

_____

2. _____

_____

3. _____

_____

4. _____

_____

Compound Sentences

Focus Similar sentences can be combined when they have closely related ideas of equal importance.

- A **compound sentence** consists of two complete sentences that are combined by using a conjunction or a semicolon.

- Use **conjunctions** such as *and, or,* or *but* to combine sentences that contain closely related ideas. Place a comma before the conjunction in a compound sentence.
    Henry rode his bike, <u>and</u> then he played kickball.

- When a **semicolon** is used to combine two sentences that contain closely related ideas, it replaces the comma and conjunction.
    Henry rode his bike; then he played kickball.

Practice Put one line under the first sentence and two lines under the second sentence that make up each compound sentence. Circle the comma and conjunction or the semicolon that is used to combine them.

1. The train whistle blew; the people got on the train.

2. Some people enjoy eating meat, but others prefer to

   eat vegetables.

3. You can do your homework now, or you can do it after

   swimming practice.

4. Everyone enjoyed the play; they applauded loudly.

5. Sally washed the dishes, and she vacuumed the downstairs.

6. Dad carried the chairs; the children brought all the lunches.

Compound Sentences *(continued)*

Rewrite the following paragraph so that it includes compound sentences. Combine sentences that are closely related by using a comma and conjunction or a semicolon.

> Greg enjoyed walking along the city sidewalks during lunch hour. His friend Kim preferred sitting in the park. Today it was raining. Greg did not want to walk in the rain. Kim did not want to sit in the rain. They decided to have lunch in a diner. Greg always ordered the same meal. He had a tuna sandwich and a glass of milk. Kim thought his meal would taste good. She ordered the same thing. By the time they finished eating, the rain had stopped.

_____

_____

_____

_____

_____

_____

_____

Apply Write three compound sentences about lunchtime at your school.

_____

_____

_____

_____

_____

_____

Literary Elements of a Story

Focus Good readers recognize the elements that distinguish a story from other literary forms, such as a play or a poem.

The elements of a story include

- a **plot**, with a beginning, middle, and end.
- **characters**, including a main character who changes in some way or learns something about himself or herself.
- a **setting**, the time and place of the story.
- a **viewpoint**, a perspective from which the story is told.

Identify Answer the following questions about "The Night Journey."

1. Who is the main character in this story? _____
   How did the character change?

   _____

   _____

   _____

2. Why is "The Night Journey" a good title for this story?

   _____

   _____

   _____

Literary Elements of a Story *(continued)*

3. "The Night Journey" is actually a story within a story.
Explain what that means.

_____

_____

_____

Apply Write the title of another story that you have read in
this unit. Then, briefly describe each of the story elements it
included and tell a little about each.

_____

_____

_____

_____

_____

_____

_____

_____

_____

_____

_____

_____

_____

_____

_____

Words in Context: Figurative and Multiple Meaning

Focus Good readers use context clues and their own experiences to help them understand phrases with figurative language or words with multiple meanings.

> - **Figurative language phrases** have vivid, descriptive words that have no literal meaning.
> - **Multiple-meaning words** have more than one meaning.

Identify Look through "The Night Journey" for examples of a multiple-meaning word and a figurative language phrase. Use the context to help you explain what you think each means.

Page: _____

Multiple-meaning word: _____

What it means: _____

_____

_____

_____

Page: _____

Figurative language phrase: _____

_____

What it means: _____

_____

_____

_____

Practice Read each passage below and decide what the
underlined words or phrases mean. Write definitions for each
underlined word or phrase. Use the context of the passages as
clues, as well as your own knowledge, to help you understand
what the words and phrases mean.

1. The clown rode a <u>unicycle</u>. He perched above the big
    wheel, moving the pedals back and forth to keep his balance.

    _____

    _____

2. The play opening on Saturday night was cause for <u>many
    tongues wagging</u> around town. Everybody was planning to
    attend. The star performer was not your <u>run-of-the-mill</u>
    community performer, but a legendary star who had grown
    up there and was finally coming home.

    _____

    _____

    _____

Apply Think about a journey you have taken. A journey
can be a physical trip or a journey in your imagination. Write
a paragraph about your journey being sure to use multiple-
meaning words and figurative language phrases.

_____

_____

_____

_____

_____

_____

_____

How Author's Viewpoint Affects the Text

Focus Writers often use quotations to support the points they wish to make in their writing.

When using quotations, a writer should

- carefully select quotations that support the points presented in his or her writing.

- transcribe the quoted passage word for word, exactly as it was spoken or written.

- identify who is quoted in the passage.

- use quotation marks to set off the quotation.

- avoid using too many quotations, because most of the text should be the writer's own.

Identify Review "Half Slave and Half Free" and complete the following.

1. What is the author's viewpoint about slavery?

_____

_____

_____

2. Find and write one statement that includes a quotation that supports your answer above.

_____

_____

_____

_____

_____

Practice Pretend that you are writing an article on each topic in the column at the left. Write the letter of the quotation by Benjamin Franklin beside the topic that it best supports.

_____ 1. Making the Best Use of Your Business Day

a. "Don't throw stones at your neighbors', if your own windows are glass."

_____ 2. Appreciating the Necessities of Life

b. "Eat to live, and not live to eat."

_____ 3. Good Nutrition Is Important to Good Health

c. "The used key is always bright."

_____ 4. Use It or Lose It

d. "Remember that time is money."

_____ 5. The Wisdom of Minding Your Own Business

e. "When the well is dry, we know the worth of water."

Apply What is your opinion of "Half Slave and Half Free"? Write a review of Russell Freedman's work that uses quotations from the selection to support your opinion.

_____

_____

_____

_____

_____

_____

_____

Using a Dictionary to Clarify Meanings

Focus Using a dictionary can help readers and writers with the meanings and spellings of words.

---

com pro mise (kom´ prə mīz´) *n.* 1. an agreement to settle a dispute, in which each side gives up something. *v.* 2. the act of giving in a little to reach an agreement.

A dictionary entry tells

- how a word is spelled and divided into syllables.

- how a word is pronounced

- what part of speech the word is (*n.* = noun, *v.* = verb, *adj.* = adjective, *adv.* = adverb, and so on).

- what the word means.

Practice and Apply Below are some words and phrases from "Half Slave and Half Free." Locate each word or phrase and write the page number on which you found it. Then look up the word or phrase in a dictionary. (You may have to look up each word in a phrase.) Based on what you find in the dictionary and its use in the sentence, write what you think the word or phrase means.

1. moral evil   Page: _____

Definition: _____

_____

_____

2. smoke screen   Page: _____

Definition: _____

_____

_____

3. popular sovereignty   Page: _____

Definition: _____

_____

_____

4. cornerstone   Page: _____

Definition: _____

_____

_____

5. monstrous injustice   Page: _____

Definition: _____

_____

_____

6. course of ultimate extinction   Page: _____

Definition: _____

_____

_____

Choose two of the words or phrases that you just defined and use each in a sentence.

_____

_____

_____

_____

_____

_____

Name _____ Date _____

Sequence

Focus Writers use time and order words to help readers understand the **sequence**, or order, of events in a story.

> • Some words that indicate time are *yesterday, tomorrow, morning, night, moment, minute, suddenly,* and *last year.*
>
> • Some words that indicate order are *first, last, after, before, during, next, finally,* and *then.*

Practice Read each sentence below and identify the time or order words. Write the time or order words on the lines provided and circle the word *time* or *order* to indicate the type of word clues they are.

1. It was raining yesterday, but the sun is shining today.

   Time or order words _____

2. When I make chocolate milk, first I put in the syrup. Then I add the milk.

   Time or order words _____

3. Tomorrow morning I will run in the big race.

   Time or order words _____

4. Suddenly, a car came speeding around the corner.

   Time or order words _____

5. After I cooked dinner, I cleaned up the kitchen.

   Time or order words _____

6. Please make your bed before you leave for school.

   Time or order words _____

Use the time and order words in the box to complete each sentence.

before	during	first
suddenly	tomorrow	then

7. _____, I am going to finish my book.

8. Julie took her turn on the swings _____ I did.

9. Nathan danced _____ the big production number.

10. Snowball _____ pounced on the ball of yarn.

11. _____, we raked the fallen leaves into a huge pile.

12. Henry took a shower; _____ he brushed his teeth.

Apply Imagine that you are one of the people making the trip across the river as it is described in "Carrying the Running-Aways." Write a paragraph that describes the trip. Use time and order words to help clarify your paragraph.

_____

_____

_____

_____

_____

_____

_____

_____

_____

_____

Name _____   Date _____

Multisyllabic Words

Focus Dividing words into syllables can help writers spell them correctly.

A **syllable** is a word part that can be said as a unit.

- It must contain a vowel or a vowel sound.
- It can either end with a vowel sound or a consonant sound.

Practice Look through samples of your own writing for multisyllabic words. List ten words, then rewrite them dividing them into syllables.

Words from Writing Sample	Words Divided into Syllables
1. _____	_____
2. _____	_____
3. _____	_____
4. _____	_____
5. _____	_____
6. _____	_____
7. _____	_____
8. _____	_____
9. _____	_____
10. _____	_____

Read the clues below. Select a word from the box to answer each clue. Write the correct word on the line.

plantation	education	vacation
fugitive	beautiful	accident

	First Clue	**Second Clue**	
11.	three syllables	a runaway	_____
12.	three syllables	mistake	_____
13.	four syllables	the process of learning	_____
14.	three syllables	pretty	_____
15.	three syllables	a large southern farm	_____
16.	three syllables	days off from school	_____

Apply Write two strategies that you can use to help you divide words and spell them correctly. Your strategies might include a rule or a mnemonic clue. Write an example word for each strategy.

Strategy: _____

_____

Example word: _____

Strategy: _____

_____

Example word: _____

Nouns and Pronouns

Focus Good writers know which pronouns to use in their writing to make their sentences clear. **Pronouns** are words that take the place of **nouns** in a sentence.

A **pronoun** must agree in number, gender, and person with the **noun** that it replaces.

- Singular pronouns replace singular nouns, and plural pronouns replace plural nouns.

- Subject pronouns replace nouns used as subjects or as predicate nominatives. Subject pronouns are *I*, *you*, *he*, *she*, *it*, *we*, and *they*.

- Object pronouns replace nouns used as objects. Object pronouns are *me*, *you*, *him*, *her*, *it*, *us*, and *them*.

- Possessive pronouns replace possessive nouns. Possessive pronouns include *my*, *your*, *his*, *her*, *its*, *our*, or *their*. Example:

  Lee already finished <u>his</u> lunch.

Practice Read the pairs of sentences below. Write a pronoun to replace the underlined word or words in the second sentence.

1. Conductors along the Underground Railroad guided escaping slaves to freedom. As a result, <u>conductors</u>

   were often in danger. _____

2. The fleeing slaves would sometimes sleep in friendly farmers' barns. The farmers would stock <u>the farmers'</u>

   barns with food and bedding. _____

3. Abolitionists along the way would tell the slaves in which direction to travel. The conductor would then lead <u>the slaves</u>

   in that direction. _____

4. Slave owners would send hunters after the slaves. The bounty hunters often took dogs with <u>the bounty hunters</u> to search

out the slaves. _____

5. None of the runaway slaves wanted to go back to the plantations. Every slave knew that <u>the slave</u> would

be punished. _____

Apply Write a pair of sentences. In the first sentence, use the words listed below. In the second sentence, replace the noun with a pronoun.

1. the children's voices _____

_____

_____

2. the table _____

_____

_____

3. Paul _____

_____

_____

4. Janet _____

_____

_____

5. report card _____

_____

_____

Name _____   Date _____

Genres

Focus A good reader can recognize and distinguish the features of different genres of literature.

Genre is the kind, or category, of writing.

- Genres include folktales and fables; myths, legends, and tall tales; realistic fiction; historical fiction; fantasy; science fiction; adventure; biography and autobiography; nonfiction (expository text); poetry; and drama.
- Authors use different writing styles for different genres.
- The content of a written work depends in part on its genre.

Identify Look through the selections you have already read in other units. Choose five selections, each from a different genre, and write the title and genre in the space provided.

1. Selection title: _____

   Genre: _____

2. Selection title: _____

   Genre: _____

3. Selection title: _____

   Genre: _____

4. Selection title: _____

   Genre: _____

5. Selection title: _____

   Genre: _____

Practice Using what you know and the information in the titles below, write the genre of each book listed.

1. *Harriet Tubman* _____

2. *Paul Bunyan and Other Larger-than-Life Tales* _____

3. *The Civil War* _____

4. *The Adventures of Tom Sawyer* _____

Apply Choose three of the genres that you listed above. Write a brief definition of each of the different genres, making sure you include information about the distinguishing features of each.

1. _____

_____

_____

_____

_____

2. _____

_____

_____

_____

_____

3. _____

_____

_____

_____

Adjectives

Focus When using adjectives to make comparisons, be sure to use the correct forms.

Comparative adjectives compare two persons, places, or things.

- For adjectives with one syllable and most adjectives with two syllables, add the ending *-er* to make them comparative.

  soft/softer   easy/easier

- For adjectives with more than two syllables, and some adjectives with two syllables, add the word *more* before the adjective to make them comparative.

  frustrating/more frustrating

Superlative adjectives compare more than two persons, places, or things.

- For adjectives with one syllable and most adjectives with two syllables, add the ending *-est* to make them superlative.

  soft/softest   easy/easiest

- For adjectives with more than two syllables, and some adjectives with two syllables, add the word *most* before the adjective.

  frustrating/most frustrating

Practice Underline the correct form of the adjective to complete each sentence.

1. Cal is the (faster, fastest) runner on the track team.

2. The French test was (harder, hardest) than the social studies test.

3. The (more exciting, most exciting) time I've ever had was when I hit a home run!

Adjectives (continued)

Fill in the blanks with the form of the adjective shown in parentheses that correctly completes each sentence.

4. I just heard the _____ news! (terrible)

5. Eli's _____ achievement was winning a prize at the Math and Science Fair. (great)

6. Compared to my two other bikes, my mountain bike

is the _____. (dependable)

7. My hair is _____ than hers. (long)

8. Mt. Everest is the _____ peak in the world. (high)

Apply Write a sentence using each form of the adjectives below.

1. noisy _____

_____

2. noisier _____

_____

3. noisiest _____

_____

4. enormous _____

_____

5. more enormous _____

_____

6. most enormous _____

_____

Cause and Effect

Charley Skedaddle

Focus Writers use **cause and effect** to make their ideas clear. Cause and effect allow readers to draw logical conclusions based on information provided earlier in the selection or on common knowledge.

- A **cause** is what makes something happen.
- An **effect** is what happens as a result of an action by a character or a situation in a story.

Identify The first part of each sentence below contains a cause. Complete each sentence so that the second part contains an effect.

1. Because Charley gave the signal, the soldiers began

   _____ the enemy.

2. Because he got scared, Charley _____.

3. Because he was in the thicket, Charley was

   _____ by the Rebels.

4. Because his soldiers pleaded with him, General Lee

   _____.

5. Because Charley was so young, the officer

   _____.

6. Because he ran away, would Noreen get

   _____?

7. Since Charley was so worn by anguish, fear, and hunger,

   _____.

Practice Use logical ideas to complete the cause-and-effect sentences below.

1. Because _____

    _____, Maggie was unable to return her library book on time.

2. Because of the mess in her room, Sylvie _____

    _____.

3. Rafael had to leave school early because _____

    _____.

4. Since there is snow outside, _____

    _____.

5. The open jar of peanut butter caused Harold to _____

    _____.

Apply Write the beginning of a nonfiction story about a historical event that you find interesting or know a lot about. Include sentences that show cause-and-effect relationships between different events in the story. Consult a reference book if you need to.

_____

_____

_____

_____

_____

_____

_____

_____

Complete Sentences

Focus Good writers state their ideas in complete sentences so that their readers will more easily understand what they have to say.

A **sentence** is a group of words that expresses a complete thought. A **complete sentence** has a subject and a predicate.

- The **subject** tells *who* or *what* the sentence is about.
- The **predicate** tells *what happened* or *what the subject did* in a sentence.
- A sentence is incomplete if it is missing a subject or a predicate.

Practice Tell whether each of the following sentences is complete or incomplete. If it is incomplete, write whether the sentence is *missing the subject* or *missing the predicate*.

1. The barn. _____

2. It's on fire. _____

3. Here comes the firetruck. _____

4. Is pulling out the hoses. _____

5. Two firefighters climbing the ladder. _____

   _____

6. Animals headed toward the fields. _____

7. The water faucet. _____

8. Was out. _____

Write a complete sentence by adding either a subject
or a predicate to the following sentence parts.

9. watching Sydney _____

_____

10. went into the dark tunnel _____

_____

11. finished first _____

_____

12. eager to get home, Josh _____

_____

Apply Charley was in one kind of battle. But there are other
kinds as well. Think about a time when you were engaged in
a battle—a disagreement with a family member or friend, a
sports competition, or trying to defend your position on a
current events topic. What did you decide to do? Why did
you make that decision? Write a paragraph describing your
thoughts about and actions during your battle. Check your
writing to make sure every sentence expresses a complete
thought or idea.

_____

_____

_____

_____

_____

_____

_____

Name _____ Date _____

Historical Fiction

Focus Knowing the characteristics of historical fiction helps readers recognize this type of story when they come across it and helps writers who want to write a story set in the past.

> **Historical fiction** is a realistic story that takes place in a specific time in the past. It may be based on historical events and real people.

Identify Below is a list of characteristics common to historical fiction. Find an example of each one from "The Siege of Vicksburg" and write it in the space provided.

1. The story is set in a particular time and place in the past.

_____

2. The plot includes events or problems from that time.

_____

_____

3. Details about things like clothing, homes, speech, transportation, and tools are correct for the time and place.

_____

_____

_____

4. The characters may include real people, and the plot may include real events.

_____

_____

_____

Practice Look through the literature in previous units for examples of stories set in the past. Identify the historical period in which each story is set. Note the clue(s) that helped you identify the period in history.

Page: _____   Title: _____

Historical period: _____

Clue(s): _____

Page: _____   Title: _____

Historical period: _____

Clue(s): _____

Apply Imagine that you are one of the soldiers who rescued Mary Byrd, Betsy, and Rosemary. Write a paragraph that tells how you rescued them. Give yourself a name and be sure to add some details that would tell a reader that your paragraph is about real people and events that happened in the past.

_____

_____

_____

_____

_____

_____

_____

_____

_____

_____

Name _____ Date _____

Prefixes

Focus Readers build their vocabulary by learning how prefixes change word meanings.

A **prefix** is a word part that is added to the beginning of a root word to form a new word.

- Knowing the meaning of the prefix can help you determine the meaning of the word.

- The prefix *un-* usually means "not" when it is attached to a root word. The prefix *re-* means "to do again."

Identify Look through "The Siege of Vicksburg" for five words that begin with the prefix *un-* and one word that begins with the prefix *re-*. Write the page number where you found the word along with the root word. Then, write the meaning of each word.

1. Prefix: *un-*   Page: _____   Root word: _____

   Meaning: _____

2. Prefix: *un-*   Page: _____   Root word: _____

   Meaning: _____

3. Prefix: *un-*   Page: _____   Root word: _____

   Meaning: _____

4. Prefix: *un-*   Page: _____   Root word: _____

   Meaning: _____

5. Prefix: *un-*   Page: _____   Root word: _____

   Meaning: _____

6. Prefix: *re-*   Page: _____   Root word: _____

   Meaning: _____

Practice Write new words by using the root words and prefixes provided below. Write your new words in the correct column on the chart.

fair	pleasant	start	willing
true	invest	play	hurt
reliable	read	direct	gain

The Prefix *un-*	The Prefix *re-*

Apply Choose three words from the chart above. Write a sentence using each word.

1. _____

_____

_____

2. _____

_____

_____

3. _____

_____

_____

Complex Sentences

Focus Writers use complex sentences to show connections between ideas.

A **complex sentence** contains one independent clause and one or more dependent clauses.

- A **clause** is a group of words that has a subject and a predicate.

- An **independent clause** can stand alone as a complete sentence.

- A **dependent clause** cannot stand alone as a complete sentence. It is usually introduced by a connecting word such as *since, who, which, if, although, because,* or *when.*

    If a dependent clause is not necessary to the meaning of the sentence, set it off from the rest of the sentence with commas.

    If a dependent clause is necessary to the meaning of the sentence, do not use commas to set if off.

    If a dependent clause begins a sentence, place a comma after the clause.

Practice Read the sentences below. Put one line under the dependent clauses and two lines under the independent clauses.

1. Since there was nothing for Betsy to eat, Amanda went for some milk and eggs.

2. When the shell crashed through the cellar wall, they ran into the tunnel.

3. They were frightened in the tunnel because they couldn't see.

4. They escaped from the tunnel when the soldiers arrived.

Read each sentence below and indicate whether it is or is not
a complex sentence. Explain your answer.

5. Jerry and his brother rode their bicycles to the beach.

_____

6. Liz raised her hand although she didn't know the answer.

_____

7. If you wash the dishes, I'll dry them.

_____

8. The green parrot in the silver cage loves to whistle.

_____

Apply Write complex sentences about "The Siege
of Vicksburg" using the dependent clauses below.

when Rosemary lit the candle

when Mary Byrd sang a lullaby

because Betsy started screaming

1. _____

_____

2. _____

_____

3. _____

_____

Possessives and Apostrophes

Focus A possessive noun shows ownership.

> • To form the possessive of a singular noun, add an apostrophe and *s* (*'s*).
>   the mother of Gao Mai   Gao Mai's mother
> • To form the possessive of a plural noun that ends in *s*, add an apostrophe (*'*).
>   the ideas of the students   the students' ideas
> • To form the possessive of a plural noun that does not end in *s*, add an apostrophe and *s* (*'s*).
>   the boots of the men   the men's boots

Practice Rewrite each phrase below, using a possessive form of the noun.

1. the plan of General Grant

_____

2. the thundering noise of the artillery

_____

3. the meals of the gunners

_____

4. the diary of a Union woman

_____

5. the passes of the men

_____

6. the noise of the gun

_____

Possessives and Apostrophes *(continued)*

Rewrite each sentence below replacing the underlined phrase
with a possessive noun.

7. <u>The skateboard that belongs to Barry</u> is on our front porch.

   _____

8. Return those garden tools to the <u>house of the Watsons</u>.

   _____

9. <u>The sister of Valerie</u> competed in the tennis tournament.

   _____

10. When you come inside the house, please bring <u>the toys that</u>

    <u>belong to the twins.</u>_____

    _____

Apply Imagine that you were at the Siege of Vicksburg. Write
a journal entry telling something that you saw or that happened
to you. Use some possessive nouns in your writing.

_____

_____

_____

_____

_____

_____

_____

_____

_____

_____

_____

Meanings of Derivatives

Focus Knowing the meaning of a root word can help you determine the meaning of its derivatives and build your vocabulary.

Adding a prefix or a suffix changes the meaning of a root word. The new word is a **derivative** of the root word.

- A **prefix** is a word part that is added to the beginning of a root word.

- A **suffix** is a word part that is added to the end of a root word.

- Adding a suffix sometimes changes the spelling of a root word.
     happy + ness = happiness
     restore + ation = restoration

- A word can have both a prefix and a suffix.
     unhappily

Practice Write the root word for each derivative.

1. rededicate   _____

2. freedom   _____

3. government   _____

4. rebirth   _____

5. devotion   _____

Write two derivatives for each of the following root words by adding a prefix or a suffix, or both, to each word. You may want to use a dictionary to check your derivatives.

6. kind   _____   _____

7. sad   _____   _____

8. inspect _____   _____

9. enjoy _____   _____

10. polite _____   _____

Apply Select two of the derivatives you wrote in Practice items 6–10 above. Write three sentences; one using the root word, one using the first derivative, and one using the second derivative. Explain how the prefixes and/or suffixes that you added changed the meaning of the root words and derivatives.

1. Root word sentence: _____

First derivative sentence: _____

_____

Second derivative sentence: _____

_____

Explanation of change in meanings: _____

_____

_____

2. Root word sentence: _____

First derivative sentence: _____

_____

Second derivative sentence: _____

_____

Explanation of change in meanings: _____

_____

_____

Commas in Direct Address and in a Series

Focus Good writers remember to use commas when they address someone directly by name and after each word or phrase before the conjunction in a series.

- In **direct address**, use one or two commas as necessary to separate the name of the person you are addressing from the rest of the sentence.

- In a **series** of three or more nouns, adjectives, verbs, or phrases, place a comma after each word or phrase before the conjunctions *and* or *or*.

Practice Rewrite the sentences below and add commas where they are needed.

1. We eat talk and play games at lunch.

   _____

2. Our meetings are held at the public library at my house

   or in the park. _____

   _____

3. Mr. Jordan may I have your autograph?

   _____

4. Come to the park with us Hannah before it gets dark.

   _____

5. It is important that you remember to turn in your work Jack.

   _____

Read the following sentences and indicate whether the commas are used in direct address or in a series. If the commas are used in a series, tell whether they are setting apart nouns, adjectives, verbs, or phrases.

6. In our house, Cissy, we keep our umbrellas on the porch.

_____

7. The squirrel ran, jumped, and scampered across the roof.

_____

8. My sister, my mother, my father, and I visited the museum.

_____

9. I love riding a roller coaster because it is fun, exciting, and scary!

_____

10. Lisa, tell me what kind of pasta you want to have for dinner.

_____

Apply Imagine that you were at Gettysburg and heard Lincoln deliver the "Gettysburg Address." Write a note to a friend describing your thoughts about the speech. Be sure to use commas in direct address and in a series in your note.

_____

_____

_____

_____

_____

_____

_____

Name _____ Date _____

Regular and Irregular Plurals

Focus Good writers spell plural nouns correctly.

- **Regular plurals** are formed by adding an *-s* or *-es* to the end of a singular noun. Some nouns require slight spelling changes to the root word.

If a noun ends in *-y*, change the *y* to *i* and add *-es*.	enemy, enemies
If a noun ends in *-s*, *-ss*, *-sh*, *-ch*, *-x*, or *-z*, add *-es*.	peach, peaches; box, boxes
If a noun ends in a vowel plus *-y*, add only *-s*.	toy, toys
If a noun ends in *-f* or *-fe*, change the *f* or *fe* to *v* and add *-es*.	half, halves

- Some **irregular plurals** are formed by changing their spellings. Others do not change at all in their plural form.
  one child, three children; one sheep, ten sheep

Practice Write the plural form for each of the following nouns found in "Buffalo Hunt."

1. pouch _____
2. fisherman _____
3. bison _____
4. wolf _____
5. century _____
6. man _____
7. baby _____

8. deer _____
9. woman _____
10. hoof _____
11. knife _____
12. saddlebag _____
13. tannery _____
14. carcass _____

Regular and Irregular Plurals (continued)

Write the singular form for each plural noun. Then, identify the
irregular plurals by circling them.

Singular	Plural	Singular	Plural
15. _____	oxen	21. _____	fish
16. _____	thieves	22. _____	canvases
17. _____	teeth	23. _____	languages
18. _____	canyons	24. _____	lives
19. _____	beliefs	25. _____	ceremonies
20. _____	activities	26. _____	supplies

Apply Imagine that you were part of one of the Native
American groups described in "Buffalo Hunt." Write a journal
entry describing a typical day as a Native American boy or girl.
Underline any plural nouns that you use.

_____

_____

_____

_____

_____

_____

_____

_____

_____

_____

_____

Prepositions and Prepositional Phrases

Focus Good writers use prepositional phrases to add details to their writing and make it more descriptive.

- A **prepositional phrase** begins with a preposition and ends with a noun or a pronoun.

     Darius caught the ball <u>near the high, wooden fence</u>.
     The first chapter <u>of the book</u> is the best.

- More than one prepositional phrase can be used in a sentence to make it clearer.

     I looked <u>under the couch</u>. I looked <u>in the closet</u>.
     I looked <u>under the couch</u> and <u>in the closet</u>.

- Some common prepositions are: *at, in, on, for, from, with, until, before, of, by, to, near,* and *under*.

- The conjunctions *and, but,* and *or* can be used to connect prepositional phrases.

Identify Look through "Buffalo Hunt." Find some examples of prepositional phrases. Write the prepositional phrases and the number of the page on which you found each one.

1. Page: _____   Phrase: _____

2. Page: _____   Phrase: _____

3. Page: _____   Phrase: _____

4. Page: _____   Phrase: _____

5. Page: _____   Phrase: _____

6. Page: _____   Phrase: _____

7. Page: _____   Phrase: _____

8. Page: _____   Phrase: _____

Prepositions and Prepositional Phrases *(continued)*

Practice Combine the following pairs of sentences into a single sentence. Use a conjunction when necessary.

1. I am climbing up the hill. I am climbing over the fence.

   _____

2. We are learning about solar energy. We are learning about it in science class.

   _____

3. Pam lives in the white house. She lives across the street.

   _____

4. I have a lot of homework. I have homework every day of the week.

   _____

5. I saw the movie in Denver. I saw it with my mother.

   _____

Apply Pretend that you have lost something that is very important to you. Write a humorous paragraph describing your search for the missing object. Use prepositional phrases to add details to your writing.

   _____

   _____

   _____

   _____

   _____

   _____

   _____

Using a Thesaurus

Focus Writers use a thesaurus to make their writing more precise.

- A **thesaurus** is a book containing synonyms and antonyms.
- A **synonym** is a word that has the same, or almost the same, meaning as another word. For example, *smart* is a synonym for *intelligent*.
- An **antonym** is a word that means the opposite of another word. For example, *exciting* means the opposite of *boring*.

Practice Read the following sentences. Use a thesaurus to find and write a synonym that could replace each underlined word.

1. Sweet Medicine had a dream that <u>prophesied</u> the coming of those who would destroy his people's way of life.

   _____

2. An <u>enormous</u> creature that the scouts called the Iron Horse terrified the people.

   _____

3. The young men of the tribe <u>hacked</u> at the iron bands that the Iron Horse rode on.

   _____

4. When the Iron Horse jumped the track, there was a <u>dreadful</u> crash.

   _____

5. The Cheyenne youth <u>unfurled</u> the cloth as he rode away.

   _____

Write a synonym and an antonym for each of the following words. Use a thesaurus to help you with your choices.

Word	Synonym	Antonym
6. moist	_____	_____
7. difficult	_____	_____
8. answer	_____	_____
9. complete	_____	_____
10. silence	_____	_____

Apply Imagine that you are one of the scouts who saw the Iron Horse for the first time. Write a paragraph that describes your experience. Use a thesaurus to make your writing exact.

_____

_____

_____

_____

_____

_____

_____

_____

_____

_____

_____

_____

Name _____   Date _____

Multisyllabic Words

The Coming of the Long Knives

Focus A **syllable** is a word part that contains a vowel sound and is said as a unit.

A syllable can end with either a **consonant sound** or a **vowel sound**.

  lib er ty   (The first syllable has a short vowel sound and ends with a consonant sound.)

  li brar y   (The first syllable ends with a long vowel sound.)

Sometimes, an affix can stand alone as its own syllable.

  re liv **ing**   (The first syllable ends with the prefix *re-*; the third ends with the suffix *-ing*.)

Identify Look through "The Coming of the Long Knives." Find words in which the first syllable ends with a long vowel sound. Write the page numbers and the words themselves on the lines below. Divide each word into syllables.

1. Page: _____ Word: _____

2. Page: _____ Word: _____

3. Page: _____ Word: _____

4. Page: _____ Word: _____

5. Page: _____ Word: _____

6. Page: _____ Word: _____

7. Page: _____ Word: _____

8. Page: _____ Word: _____

9. Page: _____ Word: _____

10. Page: _____ Word: _____

Practice Rewrite each word, dividing it into syllables.
Underline each syllable that ends in a vowel sound. Circle any
affixes. If you need help, use a dictionary.

1. radiant   _____

2. plentiful   _____

3. proclaim   _____

4. notice   _____

5. recover   _____

6. family   _____

7. studious   _____

8. delicate   _____

Apply Pretend that you are a reporter who witnessed what
happened to the Navahos who lived in Canyon de Chelly. Write
a brief article for your paper about it. After you have finished,
check to see if you used any words with syllables that end
with a vowel sound.

_____

_____

_____

_____

_____

_____

_____

_____

_____

Fact and Opinion

Focus Good writers use both facts and opinions in their writing. A good reader can tell one from the other.

- **Facts** are details that can be proven true or false.

- **Opinions** are what people think. They cannot be proven true or false.

Identify Look through "Bill Pickett: Rodeo-Ridin' Cowboy." Find examples in which the author states facts and opinions. Write the page number, identify each example as a fact or opinion, and write the example. Be sure to find examples of both.

1. Page: _____   Fact or opinion? _____

Example: _____

_____

2. Page: _____   Fact or opinion? _____

Example: _____

_____

3. Page: _____   Fact or opinion? _____

Example: _____

_____

4. Page: _____   Fact or opinion? _____

Example: _____

_____

Practice Read each sentence below and tell whether it is a fact or an opinion.

_____ **1.** In 1854, all Americans were happy to pack up their belongings and explore new land out west.

_____ **2.** As Americans began to explore the land out west, they found it inhabited by Native Americans.

_____ **3.** Lewis and Clark were among the first to journey west on a scientific expedition to explore the west.

_____ **4.** For the early Americans traveling west, a new life in a new land was worth the slow, steady trek across country.

_____ **5.** When Bill Pickett's two cousins came to visit, they bragged about their life on the trail.

_____ **6.** A cowboy's life was a good life.

Apply Explorers, hunters, naturalists, cowboys, and other adventurers traveled west. Select one of these adventurers and write a paragraph about his or her travels. You may want do some research to get factual information. Include both facts and opinions in your paragraph.

_____

_____

_____

_____

_____

_____

_____

Suffixes

Focus You can build your vocabulary by learning how suffixes change word meanings.

A **suffix** is a word part added to the end of a root word to form a new word.

- Knowing the meaning of the suffix can help you determine the meaning of the word.

- The suffix *-less* means "without."
  Careless means "without care."

- The suffix *-ful* means "full of."
  Joyful means "full of joy."

- Sometimes the spelling of a word changes slightly when a suffix is added.
  penny   penniless

Practice Add *-less* and *-ful* to each root word below to write a new word. Then write the meaning of each new word.

1. color   _____   Word meaning: _____

         _____   Word meaning: _____

2. help   _____   Word meaning: _____

         _____   Word meaning: _____

3. doubt   _____   Word meaning: _____

         _____   Word meaning: _____

4. hope   _____   Word meaning: _____

         _____   Word meaning: _____

5. rest   _____   Word meaning: _____

         _____   Word meaning: _____

Write a word that includes the suffix *-less* or *-ful* for each of the definitions below.

6. without a job _____

7. full of grace _____

8. full of beauty _____

9. without shame _____

10. without shoes _____

11. full of thanks _____

12. without pain _____

Apply Write a sentence for four of the new words that you wrote above.

1. _____

_____

_____

2. _____

_____

_____

3. _____

_____

_____

4. _____

_____

_____

Tall Tales

Focus A **tall tale** is a story that uses humor and exaggeration to tell about unusual characters and unlikely events.

A **tall tale:**

- describes the adventures of a fictional character using humorous exaggeration.

- tells a series of extraordinary events and challenges that are handled in creative ways.

Identify Look through "McBroom the Rainmaker." Find examples of sentences that are exaggeration. Write the page number where you found each sentence. Then write the sentence.

1. Page: _____ Example: _____

   _____

2. Page: _____ Example: _____

   _____

3. Page: _____ Example: _____

   _____

4. Page: _____ Example: _____

   _____

5. Page: _____ Example: _____

   _____

6. Page: _____ Example: _____

   _____

Practice Underline the words in each sentence that show exaggeration. Then, explain the real meaning of each exaggeration.

1. I was so hungry I could eat a horse.

   Explanation: _____

2. My teenage sister talks on the phone twenty-four hours a day.

   Explanation: _____

3. You have to be a millionaire to afford the new video games.

   Explanation: _____

4. Our grass grew so high that we couldn't see our house.

   Explanation: _____

Apply Reread the exaggerated sentences above. Select one as a story starter and write the first paragraph of a tall tale. Be sure to include some tall tale elements such as exaggeration, humorous characters, and unlikely events.

_____

_____

_____

_____

_____

_____

_____

_____

_____

_____

Syllable Boundary Patterns

Focus Two-syllable words can have different spelling patterns.

Two common spelling patterns are

- two consonants between two vowels. Divide words with this pattern between the two consonants, as in *pil/low.*

- three consonants between two vowels. When two consonants spell one sound or form a cluster, divide the word into syllables before or after those two consonants, as in *ex/plain* or *laugh/ter.*

Practice Rewrite each word below, dividing it into syllables. Be aware of which spelling pattern each word has when you divide it.

Word	Word Divided
1. answer	_____
2. picnic	_____
3. pumpkins	_____
4. varmints	_____
5. blossoms	_____
6. mischief	_____
7. balloons	_____
8. sprinkling	_____
9. country	_____
10. window	_____

Syllable Boundary Patterns *(continued)*

Select one of the words provided below to match each clue.
Write the word, dividing it into syllables.

empty	cotton	children	candy	complain

Clue   Word Divided into Syllables

11. people who are not grown-ups   _____

12. a sweet treat   _____

13. a kind of fabric   _____

14. to whine or grumble   _____

15. not full; vacant   _____

Apply Write a series of headlines that summarize the tall tale
"McBroom the Rainmaker." Think about the beginning, middle,
and end of the story as you plan your headlines. Write at least
five headlines and number each one. When you're finished, see
how many of the words you wrote have a spelling pattern you
studied in this lesson.

_____

_____

_____

_____

_____

_____

_____

Capitalizing Titles

Focus Titles of books, magazines, movies, plays, stories, reports, poems, and songs are capitalized.

- Capitalize the first and last words, as well as all important words, in a title.

- Capitalize the first word after a colon in a title.

- Articles, short conjunctions, and prepositions in titles are not capitalized unless they are the first or last word.
  Articles: *a, an, the*
  Conjunctions: *but, or, and*
  Prepositions: *of, to, in, on*

- A title does not end with a period, but it may end with a question mark or an exclamation point.

- In published works, titles are usually in *italics;* in handwritten text, they are underlined.

Practice Read the following titles and underline the parts that are not correct. Then explain why the underlined parts are not correct.

1. Death Of The Iron Horse

Explanation: _____

_____

2. The Land i Lost: adventures Of a boy in Vietnam by Huynh Quang Nhuong

Explanation: _____

_____

_____

Capitalizing Titles *(continued)*

The following titles are written without capital letters and, in some cases, with incomplete punctuation. Rewrite these titles correctly and underline each one.

3. learning the tuba in ten minutes

_____

4. words the right way: a student's guide to language

_____

5. where in the world is Sam Hill

_____

Apply Imagine you are asked by a publishing company to think of unique and creative titles for the following literary works. Write your titles using proper capitalization and punctuation. Underline each one. Then, compare your titles with those of your classmates.

1. A book of funny tall tales for children

_____

2. A story about the health benefits of growing your own vegetables

_____

3. A novel about a fifth grader's exploration of the western United States

_____

Words into Syllables

Focus Dividing a word into syllables and sounding out the syllables can help you spell the word correctly.

A syllable can end with either a vowel sound or a consonant sound.

fan•tas•tic   All three syllables end with a consonant sound.

so•lo   Both syllables end with a long vowel.

Practice Write each word with a line between the syllables. Underline all the syllables that end in a consonant sound.

1. basket   _____

2. interlock   _____

3. butter   _____

4. away   _____

5. watermelon   _____

6. running   _____

7. different   _____

8. biggest   _____

9. mesa   _____

10. wonderful   _____

11. number   _____

12. cactus   _____

13. thunder   _____

Words into Syllables *(continued)*

Following are six big words that contain several syllables.
Write them in the correct column on the chart, dividing them
into syllables. Underline each syllable that ends in a
consonant. If you need help, use a dictionary.

misunderstanding	reconciliation	independent
geologist	extraterrestrial	unfortunately

Four-Syllable Words	Five-Syllable Words	Six-Syllable Words

Apply Choose two of the words from the chart above. Write
a definition for each word and use it in a sentence. Use a
dictionary if you need to.

1. Word: _____

   Definition: _____

   _____

   Sentence: _____

   _____

2. Word: _____

   Definition: _____

   _____

   Sentence: _____

   _____

Possessives and Apostrophes

Focus A possessive noun shows ownership.

- To form the possessive of a singular noun, add an apostrophe and *s* (*'s*).

  the leaf of a tree   the tree's leaf

  the wheel of the bus   the bus's wheel

- To form the possessive of a plural noun ending in *s*, add only an apostrophe (*'*).

  the songs of the girls   the girls' songs

- To form the possessive of a plural noun that doesn't end in *s*, add an apostrophe and *s* (*'s*).

  the cheese of the mice   the mice's cheese

Practice Add an apostrophe or an apostrophe and *s* to the nouns below to make them possessive.

1. the family of Miguel   _____

2. the spines of the cactus   _____

3. the house of Mr. Chavez   _____

4. the games of the boys   _____

5. the eggs of our geese   _____

6. the pictures of Pedro   _____

7. the song of Gabriel   _____

8. the leaves of the bushes   _____

9. the edge of the cliff   _____

10. the sheep of the family   _____

11. the smell of the sheep   _____

Possessives and Apostrophes *(continued)*

Read the sentences below. Rewrite the phrases in parentheses
as possessive nouns.

12. (The leaves on the trees) were all changing colors.

_____

13. The boys thought (the hair of the Martians) looked green.

_____

14. What do you think happened to (the computer at the school)?

_____

15. (The sheep of Mario) were lost in the mountains.

_____

Apply Imagine that there is a natural wonder or some form of
wildlife out west that you would like to convince your parents
to take you to see. It might be the Grand Canyon, the Petrified
Forest, or a desert coyote. Do a little research and write a
paragraph describing it. Be sure to include possessive nouns in
your descriptive paragraph.

_____

_____

_____

_____

_____

_____

_____

_____

_____

Affixes and Inflectional Endings

Focus Good writers know how to add affixes
and inflectional endings correctly to root words, and they
understand how these endings change the root word.

Adding an affix to a root word changes the word's form,
function, and meaning.

- An **affix** is a word part that is added to the beginning
  or end of a word.

- A **suffix** is an affix that is added to the end of a word.

- An **inflectional ending** is a suffix, such as *-s*, *-es*, *-ed*,
  -ing, *-er*, and *-est*.

- Most words do not change their spellings when
  inflectional endings are added.

  season   season**s**   season**ed**   season**ing**

- Other words change their spellings when inflectional
  endings are added.

  carry   car**ries**   car**ried**   carrying
  plan   plans   plan**ned**   plan**ning**

Identify Circle the inflectional endings on the following
words from "Sacagawea's Journey." Underline any changes
in spelling.

1. higher   **3.** budding   **5.** buried

2. canoes   **4.** flies   **6.** shortest

Now look through "Sacagawea's Journey" and write six words
with suffixes. Circle the suffix in each word you find.

7. Page: _____   _____

8. Page: _____   _____

9. Page: _____   _____

10. Page: _____   _____

11. Page: _____   _____

12. Page: _____   _____

Practice Complete the chart by writing each root word with the following inflectional endings. Be sure to spell the words correctly.

Root Word	Add -*s* or -*es*	Add -*ed*	Add -*ing*
believe			
scare			
worry			
long			

Apply Choose one of the word families from the chart above and write one sentence for each of the three word forms that contain an inflectional ending. Identify the word's part of speech.

1. Word: _____ Part of speech: _____

Sentence: _____

_____

2. Word: _____ Part of speech: _____

Sentence: _____

_____

3. Word: _____ Part of speech: _____

Sentence: _____

_____

Subject and Verb Agreement

Focus The subject and verb of a sentence must agree. Understanding subject and verb agreement and using correct verb forms are important for good writing.

The verb must always agree in number with the subject of a sentence.

- A singular subject takes a singular verb. A plural subject takes a plural verb.

- The words *anyone, everyone, somebody, either,* and *each* take singular verbs.

- Two singular subjects connected by the word *and* take a plural verb.

- Two singular subjects connected by *or* or *nor* take a singular verb.

- A singular subject and a plural subject connected by *or* or *nor* take a verb that agrees with the word nearer to the verb.

- Be careful when there are words that come between the subject and verb. Make sure the verb agrees with the subject.

Practice Put one line under the subject and two lines under the verb in each sentence. Then, tell whether the subject and verb are singular or plural.

1. Lewis and Clark are famous for their journey into

   unknown territory. _____

2. A modern-day trip along the explorers' route takes about

   a week. _____

3. Anyone with an interest in the exploration of the American

West knows about Sacagawea. _____

4. Even today, a person with imagination can sense the excitement

of that long and perilous journey. _____

Apply Write sentences with present-tense verbs that contain
the following words used as subjects. Make sure your subjects
and verbs agree.

1. somebody _____

_____

2. Mother and the boys _____

_____

3. everyone _____

_____

4. the team _____

_____

5. I _____

_____

6. Kyle or Laura _____

_____

7. the houses across the street _____

_____

8. the Greens _____

_____

Using a Thesaurus

Focus Using a thesaurus can help writers find the exact word to communicate what they mean and add variety to their writing.

A **thesaurus** is a book of synonyms and antonyms.

- A **synonym** is a word that has the same or almost the same meaning as another word.

- An **antonym** is a word that has the opposite meaning of another word.

- The words in a thesaurus are usually arranged in alphabetical order. Some thesauruses, however, are arranged by topics.

- An entry for a word in a thesaurus includes the part of speech, synonyms for that word, and sometimes antonyms of that word.

Practice Use the thesaurus entries below to answer the following questions.

> **precious** *adj.* costly, valuable *Ant.* cheap.
>
> **journey** *n. & v.* 1. *n.* trip, tour; voyage, cruise; expedition; hike; pilgrimage; caravan, trek. 2. *v.* travel; voyage, sail, cross; tour, roam, range, venture, explore; ride, drive, motor. See TRAVEL.

1. Which word has an antonym? Write the word and its antonym.

   _____   _____

2. List three synonyms for the noun *journey*.

   _____

3. What part of speech is the word *precious*? _____

4. What part of speech is the word *journey*? _____

Use a thesaurus to find synonyms for the words below.

5. the noun *reunion*   _____

6. the verb *cultivate*   _____

7. the adjective *lonely*   _____

8. the adjective *homesick*   _____

9. the verb *whisper*   _____

10. the noun *memory*   _____

Apply Write a paragraph about a favorite vacation or trip.
Then, use a thesaurus to help you replace the words you use
a lot with more interesting choices. Cross out each word you
want to replace and write a synonym above it.

_____

_____

_____

_____

_____

_____

_____

_____

_____

_____

Adverbs

Focus Good writers use adverbs to add interest and precision to their writing.

An **adverb** describes a verb, an adjective, or another adverb.

- Adverbs tell when, where, how, how much, or how often.
- Many adverbs are formed by adding *-ly* to an adjective. Sometimes the spelling of the word changes when the *-ly* ending is added, as in *happy* and *happily*.

You can use adverbs to make comparisons.

- If an adverb ends in *-ly*, use *more* to compare two actions; use *most* to compare more than two actions.
- For other adverbs, add the ending *-er* to compare two actions. To compare more than two actions, add the ending *-est*. Sometimes the spelling of the word changes when these endings are added.

Identify Look through "Tanya's Reunion" for the author's use of adverbs. Write eight that you find.

1. Page: _____   Adverb: _____

2. Page: _____   Adverb: _____

3. Page: _____   Adverb: _____

4. Page: _____   Adverb: _____

5. Page: _____   Adverb: _____

6. Page: _____   Adverb: _____

7. Page: _____   Adverb: _____

8. Page: _____   Adverb: _____

Adverbs (*continued*)

Practice Underline the adverb in each sentence below. Write whether the adverb tells when, where, how, how much, or how often.

1. As they pulled away in the car, Gina waved sadly to

   her friends. _____

2. The baby woke up late in the morning. _____

3. I must have left my cap somewhere on the playground.

   _____

4. A cheetah moves more silently than an elephant does.

   _____

5. Adrian threw the softball the farthest. _____

Apply Rewrite each sentence below, adding an adverb to make it more descriptive.

1. Mac shouted at the referee. _____

   _____

2. We reached the city. _____

   _____

3. The dog ate his dinner. _____

   _____

4. You can tell that he is a dancer by the way he moves. _____

   _____

5. The truck got stuck in the mud. _____

   _____

Meanings of Words in Context

Focus When words in a story have multiple or figurative meanings, readers can use context clues or their own experiences to help them figure out what the words mean.

- **Multiple-meaning words** are words with more than one meaning.

- **Figurative language**, or figure of speech, is vivid, descriptive language that has meaning beyond its literal, or word-for-word, meaning.

- Simile, metaphor, personification, and onomatopoeia are different types of figurative language.
    Simile: The rainbow spread across the sky like
      a colored snake.
    Metaphor: The rainbow was a colored snake spread
      across the sky.
    Personification: The trees stood tall and proud.
    Onomatopoeia: "Squeeeak" went the rusty door
      on its hinges.

Practice Read the following sentences with figurative language and write an explanation of what each really means.

1. The suitcase was as light as a feather. _____

   _____

2. The tree's shoulders were bowed under its blanket of snow.

   _____

   _____

3. The washing machine sounded like a locomotive. _____

   _____

   _____

Meanings of Words in Context (*continued*)

4. The sound was music to the plumber's ears. _____

_____

_____

5. The machine coughed, sighed, and wheezed to a stop. _____

_____

_____

Apply Read the following sentences and use the context and
your own knowledge to write a literal and figurative definition
for the underlined word.

1. The vast ocean <u>swallows</u> up the tiny sailboat.

Literal meaning: _____

_____

Figurative meaning: _____

_____

2. The cup and saucer <u>danced</u> across the floor when the table fell over.

Literal meaning: _____

_____

Figurative meaning: _____

_____

3. His hands are <u>sandpaper</u>.

Literal meaning: _____

_____

Figurative meaning: _____

_____

Adjectives

Focus When using adjectives to make comparisons, be sure to use the correct forms.

Comparative adjectives compare two persons, places, or things.

- To compare two persons, places, or things, add the ending -*er* to most one-syllable adjectives and some two-syllable adjectives. For adjectives with more than two syllables, and for some two-syllable adjectives, use the word *more.*

  smaller   happier   more graceful

Superlative adjectives compare more than two persons, places, or things.

- To compare more than two persons, places, or things, add the ending -*est* to most one-syllable adjectives and to some two-syllable adjectives. For adjectives with more than two syllables, and for some two-syllable adjectives, use the word *most.*

  smallest   happiest   most graceful

Practice Underline the comparative and superlative adjectives in the sentences below. Then, tell what and how many are being compared.

1. I am the tallest student in my class.

_____

2. The cat was more suspicious of the ball than the dog was.

_____

3. The pear was heavier than the banana.

_____

Adjectives (continued)

Write sentences that use adjectives to compare the following persons, places, or things.

4. more than two cities: _____

_____

5. two vegetables: _____

_____

6. two planets: _____

_____

7. more than two sisters: _____

_____

8. three cars: _____

_____

Apply Write a paragraph that compares two or more of your favorite places to visit. The places could be near where you live or far away. Be sure to use adjectives to make your writing descriptive and interesting.

_____

_____

_____

_____

_____

_____

_____

_____

Prefixes

Focus You can build your vocabulary by learning how prefixes change word meanings.

A **prefix** is a word part added to the beginning of a root word.

Root Word	Prefix	Meaning	New Word	Meaning
arrange	*pre-*	before	prearrange	arrange before
usual	*un-*	not	unusual	not usual
satisfied	*dis-*	not	dissatisfied	not satisfied
think	*re-*	again	rethink	think again

Identify Look through "Alberic the Wise." Find examples of words the writer has used that contain prefixes. Write each word, underlining the prefix. Then, write the word's meaning.

1. Page: _____ Word: _____ Meaning: _____

2. Page: _____ Word: _____ Meaning: _____

3. Page: _____ Word: _____ Meaning: _____

4. Page: _____ Word: _____ Meaning: _____

5. Page: _____ Word: _____ Meaning: _____

6. Page: _____ Word: _____ Meaning: _____

7. Page: _____ Word: _____ Meaning: _____

8. Page: _____ Word: _____ Meaning: _____

9. Page: _____ Word: _____ Meaning: _____

10. Page: _____ Word: _____ Meaning: _____

Practice Build new words by using prefixes from the box on page 175 and adding them to the root words below.

Root Words	New Words
1. write	_____
2. like	_____
3. protected	_____
4. judge	_____
5. comfort	_____
6. own	_____
7. build	_____
8. appear	_____
9. happy	_____
10. exist	_____

Apply Choose three of the new words above and write a sentence for each.

1. _____

_____

_____

2. _____

_____

_____

3. _____

_____

_____

Pronoun Referents

Focus Good writers use the correct pronouns and pronoun referents so their writing is clear.

A **pronoun** is a word that takes the place of a noun. The **pronoun referent,** or **antecedent,** is the noun referred to by the pronoun. A pronoun must agree with the noun it replaces.

- Singular pronouns take the place of singular nouns.

- Plural pronouns take the place of plural nouns.

- Subject pronouns take the place of nouns used as subjects.

- Object pronouns take the place of nouns used as objects.

- Possessive pronouns take the place of possessive nouns.

Practice Write the correct pronouns in the sentences.

1. Jennifer went upstairs. _____ wanted to find her books. (She/Her)

2. Tim asked Matt and Derek to the movies. He was glad

   _____ could go. (they/them)

3. When Jim bumped the pitcher, _____ fell over and water spilled out. (it/he)

Underline the pronouns in the sentences below. Tell which noun each pronoun refers to.

4. Liz apologized to Mr. McKenzie for breaking the window. He accepted her apology.

   _____

5. Mr. McKenzie got out the ladder and placed it against the house.

   _____

6. Liz watched anxiously as her neighbor climbed the ladder.

_____

7. Then, Tom and Tricia came out of the house. They stood with

Liz and watched, too. _____

_____

8. Mr. McKenzie reached the window. He took out his measuring

tape, but dropped it on the ground. _____

_____

Apply Alberic was influenced by a traveler he met. Write a
paragraph about someone who has influenced you. Be sure
to use pronouns correctly.

_____

_____

_____

_____

_____

_____

_____

_____

_____

_____

_____

_____

Name _____   Date _____

Suffixes

Focus You can build your vocabulary by learning how suffixes change word meanings.

• A **suffix** is a syllable added to the end of a root word.

Root Word	Suffix	Meaning	New Word	Meaning
empty	-ness	quality of	emptiness	quality of being empty
enjoy	-ment	state of	enjoyment	state of being enjoyed
child	-ish	to be like	childish	to be like a child
civil	-ize	make or become	civilize	to make civil

Practice Identify the suffix in each word and write the meaning of the word.

1. yellowish   _____   _____

2. development   _____   _____

3. finalize   _____   _____

4. happiness   _____   _____

5. government   _____   _____

6. recklessness   _____   _____

7. foolish   _____   _____

8. contentment   _____   _____

9. weariness   _____   _____

10. legalize   _____   _____

Suffixes *(continued)*

Build new words by choosing suffixes from the box on page 179 and adding them to the root words below.

Root Words	New Words
11. thoughtful	_____
12. excite	_____
13. clown	_____
14. deputy	_____
15. achieve	_____
16. general	_____
17. harsh	_____
18. equip	_____

Apply Choose three of the new words above and write a sentence for each.

1. _____

_____

_____

2. _____

_____

_____

3. _____

_____

_____

Name _____   Date _____

Compound and
Complex Sentences

Focus Writers use compound and complex sentences to show
connections between ideas.

A **compound sentence** consists of two complete sentences
that are closely related. The sentences can be combined into
one sentence by using a conjunction plus a comma, or
a semicolon.

- Use **conjunctions** such as *and, or, so,* or *but* to combine
  sentences that contain closely related ideas. Place a
  comma before the conjunction in a compound sentence.

- When a **semicolon** is used to combine two sentences
  that contain closely related ideas, it replaces the comma
  and conjunction.

A **complex sentence** consists of an independent clause and
one or more dependent clauses.

- A **dependent clause** cannot stand by itself.

- An **independent clause** can stand by itself as a
  complete sentence.

Practice Underline the two sentences that make up each of
the following compound sentences. Circle the comma and
conjunction or the semicolon used to combine them.

1. The bus stopped at the bus stop, but no one got on.

2. We need to work on our project tonight; it is due in two days.

3. The party can be at the lake, or it can be at the pool.

4. Brad was at the park, but he had to go home.

5. Julilly and Liza were frightened, but they were determined

   never to be slaves again.

Compound and Complex Sentences *(continued)*

Underline the dependent clause in each of the complex
sentences below. Put two lines under the independent clause
in each sentence.

   6. Jake always avoids the house where the dog bit him.

   7. We are learning how volcanoes are born.

   8. Although I was late for school, I didn't miss the field trip
   to the museum.

Read each sentence. Decide whether it is a compound
or a complex sentence.

   9. Computers help us find out about the weather, and they also

   are used to report news from around the world. _____

   10. Joey believes everything that anyone tells him. _____

   11. I can't see the play tonight, but I can go tomorrow night. _____

   12. Did JoAnna tell you that she won the contest? _____

Apply Choose a paragraph from something that you have
written recently. Rewrite the paragraph using compound
and complex sentences.

_____

_____

_____

_____

_____

_____

_____

_____